Healthy Kitchen™

Year-Round Fresh

150 recipes that make the most of what's in season!

WW Publishing Group

Managing editor: Valeria Bloom

Food editor: Eileen Runyan

Writer and project editor: Jackie Mills, MS, RD

Contributing editors: Lisa Chernick, Leslie Fink, MS, RD

Nutrition consultant: Linda Wang

Recipe developers: Dina Cheney, Julie Hartigan, Paul Piccuito, Carol Prager, Sarah Reynolds, and Julia Rutland

Creative director: Ed Melnitsky

Design director: Daniela A. Hritcu

Designer: Arlene Lappen

Production manager: Alan Biederman

Photo director: Marybeth Dulany

Photographer: John Kernick

Food stylist: Carrie Purcell

Prop stylist: Alistair Turnbull

SKU #61013
Printed in the USA

Front cover:
Pasta and spring vegetables with feta, page 39

Back cover:
Roasted beet and carrot salad, page 130

About WW

WW is a global wellness company and the world's leading commercial weight-management program. We inspire millions of people to adopt healthy habits for real life. Through our engaging digital experience and face-to-face group meetings, members follow our livable and sustainable program that encompasses healthy eating, physical activity, and a positive mindset. With more than five decades of experience in building communities and our deep expertise in behavioral science, we aim to deliver wellness for all. To learn more about the WW approach to healthy living, please visit ww.com. For more information about our global business, visit our corporate website at corporate.ww.com.

Skillet ratatouille
with eggs, 56

Contents

About our recipes

While losing weight isn't only about what you eat, WW realizes the critical role it plays in your success and overall good health. That's why our philosophy is to offer great-tasting, easy recipes that are nutritious as well as delicious. Our recipes emphasize the kinds of healthy foods we love: lots of fresh fruits and vegetables, most of which have 0 SmartPoints value, and lean proteins, some of which have 0 SmartPoints and others that are low in SmartPoints. We also try to ensure that our recipes fall within the recommendations of the U.S. Dietary Guidelines for Americans—lower in saturated fat and sugar with plenty of fruits and vegetables, lean proteins, and low-fat dairy—so they support a diet that promotes health and reduces the risk for disease. If you have special dietary needs, consult with your health-care professional for advice on a diet that is best for you, then adapt these recipes to meet your specific nutritional needs.

Get started, keep going, and enjoy good nutrition

At WW, we believe that eating well makes life better, no matter where you are in your weight-loss journey. These tasty recipes are ideal, whether you're just getting started or have already reached your goals on the SmartPoints system. Unlike other weight-loss programs, which focus solely on calories, the SmartPoints system guides you toward healthier foods that are lower in sugar and saturated fat, and higher in protein. But this isn't a diet—all food is "in." Eating well should be fun, energizing, and delicious, so that healthy food choices become second nature. To get maximum satisfaction, keep the following in mind:

- On the WW Freestyle™ program, eating a mix of foods (rather than all ZeroPoint™ meals) can help you avoid feeling bored or deprived. Remember, there's room for all SmartPoints foods in your plan—variety is key to a healthy and livable eating style.

- SmartPoints values are given for each recipe. The SmartPoints value for each ingredient is assigned based on the number of calories and the amount of saturated fat, sugar, and protein in each ingredient. The SmartPoints values for each ingredient are then added together and divided by the number of servings, and the result is rounded.

- Recipes include approximate nutritional information: They are analyzed for Calories (Cal), Total Fat, Saturated Fat (Sat Fat), Sodium (Sod), Total Carbohydrates (Total Carb), Sugar, Dietary Fiber (Fib), and Protein (Prot). The nutritional values are obtained from the WW database, which is maintained by registered dietitians.

- To boost flavor, we often include fresh herbs or a squeeze of citrus instead of increasing the salt. If you don't need to restrict your sodium intake, feel free to add a touch more salt.

- Look for these symbols throughout the book to choose recipes that fit best with your dietary needs:

  - **Vegetarian:** Recipes that contain no animal flesh foods or products made from animal flesh, though they may contain eggs and dairy products.

  - **Vegan:** Recipes that contain no animal flesh foods, eggs, dairy products, or honey.

  - **Gluten free:** Recipes that contain no wheat, barley, or rye, or any products that are made from these ingredients.

  - **Dairy free:** Recipes that contain no milk from any animal and no products made from animal milk.

  - **Nut free:** Recipes that contain no tree nuts or peanuts.

    Note: Recipes conform to the icon designations, but the tip serving suggestions may not.

- Recipe tips have a SmartPoints value of 0 unless otherwise stated.

- For information about the WW plan, please visit ww.com/us/m/cms/plan-basics.

Calculations not what you expected?

SmartPoints values for the recipes in this book are calculated without counting the ZeroPoint foods—fruits, most vegetables, and some lean proteins that are part of the plan. However, the nutritional information does include the nutrient content of these ingredients. This means you may notice discrepancies with the SmartPoints value you calculate using the nutrition information provided for the recipe versus the SmartPoints value listed for the recipe. That's because the SmartPoints values for the recipes that contain ZeroPoint ingredients have been adjusted to reflect those ingredients, while the nutrition information provided includes the nutrition for all of the ingredients. For tracking purposes, use the SmartPoints value listed for the recipe. Also, please note, when fruits and veggies are liquefied or pureed (as in a smoothie), their nutrient content is incorporated into the recipe calculations. These nutrients can increase the SmartPoints.

Alcohol is included in our SmartPoints calculations. Because alcohol information is generally not included on nutrition labels, it's not an option you can include when using the handheld or online SmartPoints calculator or the WW app. But since we include the alcohol information that we get from our database in our recipes, you might notice discrepancies between the SmartPoints you see here in our recipes and the values you get using the calculator. The SmartPoints listed for our recipes are the most accurate values.

Choosing ingredients

As you learn to eat more healthfully and add more wholesome foods to your meals, consider these:

- **Lean meats and poultry**
  Purchase lean meats and poultry, and trim them of all visible fat before cooking. When poultry is cooked with the skin on, we recommend removing the skin before eating. Nutritional information for recipes that include meat, poultry, and fish is based on cooked skinless, boneless portions (unless otherwise stated) with the fat trimmed.

- **Seafood**
  Whenever possible, our recipes call for seafood that is sustainable and deemed the most healthful for human consumption so that your choice of seafood is not only good for the oceans but also good for you. For more information about the best seafood choices and to download a pocket guide, go to the Environmental Defense Fund at seafood.edf.org, the Monterey Bay Aquarium at seafoodwatch.org, or the Safina Center at safinacenter.org.

- **Produce**
  For the best flavor, maximum nutrient content, and the lowest prices, buy fresh, local produce such as vegetables, leafy greens, and fruits in season. Rinse them thoroughly before using, and keep a supply of cut-up vegetables and fruits in your refrigerator for convenient healthy snacks.

- **Whole grains**
  Explore your market for whole-grain products such as whole wheat and whole-grain breads and pastas, brown rice, bulgur, barley, cornmeal, whole wheat couscous, oats, farro, and quinoa to enjoy with your meals.

Cooking with the seasons

It's easy to be a great cook when you start with the freshest foods available and prepare them without fuss.

Nothing tastes better—or is better for you—than a meal inspired by fresh seasonal produce. Cooking with each season's best fruits and vegetables makes it simple to prepare satisfying, flavor-packed dishes. Fresh food tastes great naturally, so you don't have to use complicated cooking techniques or a lot of spices and seasonings to make it delicious. And, when you're using generous amounts of fresh produce, you're already making healthy choices.

Every seasonal change brings an abundant crop of wholesome fruits and vegetables to enjoy and the recipes in this book help you prepare them to their best advantage. In every recipe, at least one kind of produce is used to create dishes that taste bright, fresh, and irresistibly flavorful. We encourage you to pass by frozen asparagus in April and use the first tender stalks of spring to make a Ham and goat cheese frittata with spring vegetables (page 5), skip frozen peaches in August and use fresh local fruit to make Raspberry-peach smoothies (page 65), and in October, to say no to canned pumpkin and pick up a fresh sugar pumpkin for Pumpkin-ginger bisque (page 128).

Overflowing farmers' markets are the place of choice to purchase fresh produce during the abundant harvest months. In "Farmers' market shopping guide" on page x, you'll find information on locating a market, shopping tips, and the advantages of shopping local. Sometimes you just can't shop for local produce and that's OK. In most areas, farmers' markets shut down for the winter and sometimes in time-crunched summer months, you don't have time to make the trip to buy from your favorite farmers. But supermarkets offer convenience and an abundance of fresh foods all year long. With the advice in "Supermarket shopping guide" on page xii, we give you tips on how to choose the best grocery store and advice for making the most of the money you spend there.

We're not saying everything you cook needs to be fresh. Pantry staples like canned beans, tomatoes, and broths, whole grains and whole wheat pasta, oils and vinegars as well as condiments like mustards, soy sauce, and hot sauce are essential for making healthful home-cooked weeknight meals. With a well-stocked pantry and the fresh foods you pick up at the supermarket or the farmers' market each week, you'll have everything you need to make appetizing and easy meals.

In this book, you'll find chapters with recipes arranged according to the seasons, with a bonus chapter of 20-minute main dishes, all of which start with fresh produce, too. At the beginning of each of the seasonal chapters, we've included a list of foods typically available at that time of year, but depending on where you live, the varieties may vary. Enjoy trying them all throughout the year.

Once you discover the difference that cooking with healthy seasonal produce makes, you'll love how incorporating fresh fruits and vegetables, lean proteins, and good fats—the cornerstone of the SmartPoints system—helps you feel nourished, healthy, and satisfied. With food this tempting, delicious is always in season.

Peach, tomato, and avocado salad, 72

Farmers' market shopping guide

With more people wanting to know where their food is grown, farmers' markets are proliferating all over the country. Here's how to find one, the benefits of shopping local, and how to make the most of every trip.

How to find a farmers' market.

The United States Department of Agriculture (USDA) website offers a farmers' market directory where you can search by zip code to find markets in your area (search. ams.usda.gov/farmersmarkets). Check your state's Department of Agriculture website as well, which may give more detailed information such as markets specializing in organic produce, listings of pick-your-own farms, and locations of roadside produce stands. Another excellent source for finding local produce is LocalHarvest.org.

What "local" means at your market.

Individual farmers' markets are run with different rules on what defines "local." Some markets will stipulate that the food sold at the market must be grown within a certain radius, say within 50 or 100 miles of the market. At other markets, you may see tropical fruits being sold in Northern states or produce from California being sold in a "farmers' market" on the East Coast. The only way to find out is to observe what is being sold and get to know the farmers.

Local or organic?

In a perfect world, you would have both. But because in most parts of the country eating locally year-round would make for limited food choices and many farmers do not grow organically, it's a choice that you'll need to make based on the factors that are most important to you. Not "certified organic" doesn't necessarily mean food is not "organic." Organic certification by the USDA is a costly and time-consuming process that requires farmers to submit an application and undergo inspection. Some farmers choose not to be certified because of the costs involved or for political reasons. Ask each farmer if he's certified. If he isn't, ask him how his produce is grown—how he manages pests, what types of fertilizers he uses, and whether he plants genetically engineered seeds. Most farmers are happy to talk to customers in detail about how they grow their crops.

Consider a CSA.

Community Supported Agriculture is a system that allows consumers to buy a "share" of vegetables or fruits from a farmer in the same region. Typically, payment is made to the farmer before the season starts to provide money for seeds, equipment, repairs, and labor. Weekly shares of produce are picked up at the farm or a central location throughout the growing season. To find a CSA in your area, go to localharvest.org.

Local foods are more nutritious.

Because foods—whether or not they're organic—begin to lose nutrients as soon as they're picked, locally grown foods, which travel a shorter distance to market, are more nutritious. Locally grown perishable fruits and vegetables are also more likely to be picked at peak ripeness, since they're harvested and sold within a day or two.

Local food lasts longer.

Eating fresh seasonal foods that are locally grown means the produce is likely to stay fresher a day or two longer once you get it home. Local foods haven't had to be packaged and shipped thousands of miles, so they're fresher when you buy them. And fresher food tastes better, too.

Shopping local supports your community.

Buying locally produced foods helps support businesses in your area, promotes the success of small farms, and lets you connect with friends and neighbors while shopping in a convivial atmosphere.

Natural food markets may not be best option.

Natural food markets, which sell organic and specialty foods, have an aura of good health, but you'll probably do just as well with most items at a regular supermarket. And, not all foods in these markets are good for you. Just because a food is labeled "natural" or "organic" doesn't mean it's nutritious. Shop at natural food markets only for those items that your regular supermarket doesn't carry, like unusual whole grains, gluten-free flours, and specialty spices.

Fruits, veggies & so much more

During peak growing season in your region, you will almost always get fresher, better quality, more inexpensive produce at a farmers' market than you will at the supermarket. But there are even more advantages:

Your farmers' market may be open seasonally—only during summer and early fall harvest times. Some markets, however, are open year-round, offering root vegetables and apples as well as cheeses, meats, poultry, seafood, eggs, grains and dried beans, breads, honey, and even wine to go with your meal. Some farmers have greenhouses and may offer a larger selection of tender vegetables year-round. If supporting sustainability and local commerce and knowing where your food comes from are important to you, you may be able to do almost all your food shopping at a farmers' market.

Farmers' markets can provide a wealth of cooking and recipe ideas. If you're unfamiliar with a type of produce, ask the farmer the best way to prepare it. Chances are he has been growing and cooking the produce varieties he sells for years. Check to see if your market sponsors cooking demonstrations or cooking classes. Many have events featuring local chefs or cookbook authors serving up fresh ideas for what's in season.

Market shopping logistics

See these tips to plan ahead for farmers' market shopping to make your visit more enjoyable and rewarding.

- If your market is far away and you plan on buying perishable items such as meats or seafood, put a cooler in the car for transporting them home.

- Most farmers offer bags, but in the spirit of sustainability and environmental concerns, carry your own reusable bags to the market.

- Go with a general idea of what you are going to buy. Vegetables for dinner for three nights? Enough fruit for a week of snacks? Once you arrive, let the market be your guide on specifics—just don't buy more than you'll use before your next trip.

Supermarket shopping guide

Farmers' markets may be the go-to choice for shopping for fresh fruits and vegetables in warm weather months, but for most of us—even in summer—a weekly spin through the supermarket is essential. Consider the following suggestions:

Choose a busy market that's convenient.

A full parking lot may be the best indication that you'll find the freshest food inside the store. Where there's a lot of turnover, you'll have a better chance of getting the best quality produce available. Shopping at a market near where you live or on a route you take often to get to work will save you time and will be better for the environment, since you don't have to burn extra fuel to get there.

Shop at a store where the focus is on fresh foods.

Fruits and vegetables, lean meats and poultry, seafood, and low-fat dairy products are the basics for eating healthfully. Budget your food dollars for stores that offer the freshest, best quality options for these perishable items. Avoid supermarkets where produce is limited in selection or wrapped in plastic. If meats are not well-trimmed or if the seafood counter smells less than fresh, shop elsewhere. Choose a store that offers a full range of fat-free and low-fat yogurt, milk, and cheese.

Look for local foods at the grocery store.

If you can't make it to a farmers' market every week during the summer, a store that works with local farmers to sell their fresh produce is a fantastic choice. Everyone wins: You get fresh food in a convenient location, the farmer makes a profit by selling a large quantity of produce, and the market makes money by attracting customers who are enticed by the local foods.

Choose produce without a brand—almost always.

Unless you can tell the quality of the product just by looking (for example if the branded lettuce is fresh and crisp-looking and the non-branded is wilted) you'll save money by buying non-branded produce. Brands cost companies money to market and advertise and they pass those costs on to the consumer.

Buy foods whole and prep them yourself.

Fresh veggies and fruits will be fresher and last longer if you wash, shred, peel, and cut them yourself. But, if you are in a time crunch and you'll use them immediately, these prepped and ready-to-use foods let you eat healthy in a hurry.

Is organic worth the price?

Produce labeled organic must be grown without synthetic pesticides or fertilizers and no GMOs can be used. For meats, eggs, and dairy products to be labeled organic, the animals that produce them must have outdoor access to organic land, must eat organic feed, and can't have consumed hormones or antibiotics. Though there is no scientific proof that organic food is more nutritious than non-organic, some people prefer not to eat food that's grown using chemical pesticides or fertilizers or that's a genetically modified organism (GMO). To make the most of your food budget, see "Smart Shopper Lists" (at right) for lists of the cleanest and dirtiest produce.

Get fresh

Keep these tips in mind as you shop the produce aisle at your supermarket every week.

Freshness is easy to discern.
Wilted lettuce, wrinkled apples, and shriveled berries are obvious to even the most inexperienced shopper. If what you want looks past its peak, choose a different fruit or vegetable, and if many of the offerings are not top quality, find another supermarket.

Try a new fruit or vegetable every week.
If you're just starting to incorporate more produce into your meals and snacks, you may see some unfamiliar foods in the produce section. Buy one item you've never tried each week and check the recipes here or use online sources for the best ways to prepare your discoveries. Chances are you'll love most of the foods you sample.

Select a variety.
Choose several kinds of produce each week. Diversity keeps you from getting bored and each fruit and vegetable offers different nutrients to nourish your body. Even if you love apples, choose various kinds so you can enjoy the unique flavor and texture of each one.

Buy only what you'll eat.
The vast majority of fruits and veggies are ZeroPoint™ foods and good for you, so eat lots of them. But don't let your enthusiasm lead you to buy more than you and your family can eat before your next shopping trip.

Make a plan for winter.
The only time it makes sense to overbuy is when produce is at its peak. Buy extra berries to freeze to enjoy with cold-weather oatmeal or make fresh tomato sauce for quick weeknight pasta meals when the temperature drops.

Smart shopper lists

Every year, the Environmental Working Group (EWG), designates two lists of produce; one with the most and one with the least amounts of pesticides. They're known as the Dirty Dozen and Clean 15.

Dirty Dozen
- Apples
- Bell peppers
- Celery
- Cherries
- Grapes
- Nectarines
- Peaches
- Pears
- Potatoes
- Spinach
- Strawberries
- Tomatoes

Clean 15
- Asparagus
- Avocados
- Broccoli
- Cabbage
- Cantaloupe
- Cauliflower
- Corn
- Eggplant
- Honeydew
- Kiwi
- Mangos
- Onions
- Papayas
- Peas (frozen)
- Pineapples

Fennel

Artichokes

Chives

Strawberries

Leeks

Chapter 1

Spring

Rejuvenate your spirit with the vibrant flavors of this gentle season.

Rhubarb

Sugar snap peas

Scallions

Radishes

Mint

In this chapter

What's in season

- Artichokes
- Asparagus
- Avocados
- Baby carrots
- Baby potatoes
- Baby salad greens
- Cucumbers
- Dill, mint, and chives
- Fava beans
- Green peas
- Leeks
- Mangoes
- Radishes
- Rhubarb
- Scallions
- Strawberries
- Sugar snap peas
- Vidalia onions
- Watercress

Asparagus and pea pancakes

Serves 4

½ **pound thin asparagus, trimmed and cut into 1-inch pieces**

½ **cup fresh shelled green peas or frozen baby peas**

½ **cup whole wheat flour**

½ **cup all-purpose flour**

1 **teaspoon baking powder**

½ **teaspoon salt**

¼ **teaspoon baking soda**

1¼ **cups low-fat buttermilk**

1 **large egg**

2 **scallions, thinly sliced**

3 **tablespoons chopped fresh dill**

1 **(6-ounce) container plain fat-free Greek yogurt**

¼ **cup crumbled feta cheese**

1 Bring large pot of water to boil over medium-high heat; stir in asparagus and peas. Cook just until crisp-tender, about 1 minute. Drain in colander and rinse under cold running water; drain again and pat dry with paper towels.

2 Whisk together whole wheat flour, all-purpose flour, baking powder, salt, and baking soda in large bowl.

3 Whisk together buttermilk and egg in medium bowl. Add buttermilk mixture, asparagus and peas, scallions, and 2 tablespoons of dill to flour mixture. Stir just until blended.

4 Heat nonstick griddle or large nonstick skillet over medium heat. Pour batter by scant ⅓-cup measures onto griddle. Cook until bubbles begin to appear at edges of pancakes, about 2 minutes. Turn and cook until puffed and browned, about 2 minutes longer.

5 Meanwhile, stir together yogurt, feta, and remaining 1 tablespoon dill in small bowl. Serve pancakes with yogurt sauce.

5 **SmartPoints value per serving** (2 pancakes and 1½ tablespoons sauce): 235 Cal, 5 g Total Fat, 2 g Sat Fat, 748 mg Sod, 34 g Total Carb, 7 g Sugar, 4 g Fib, 16 g Prot.

Tip
Give pasture-raised eggs from free-range chickens a try. They can cost $2 to $3 more a dozen than supermarket eggs, but the flavor is richer, and in most cases, the chickens are raised more humanely.

Ham and goat cheese frittata
with spring vegetables

Ham and goat cheese frittata with spring vegetables

Serves 4

2	teaspoons unsalted butter
¼	pound baby red potatoes, thinly sliced
6	ounces thin asparagus, cut into 1-inch pieces
⅓	cup thinly sliced leek, white and light green parts only, or chopped sweet onion
2	teaspoons minced fresh thyme
½	cup chopped lean ham
6	large egg whites
3	large eggs
½	teaspoon salt
½	teaspoon black pepper
¼	cup crumbled goat cheese

1 Preheat oven to 350°F.

2 Melt butter in 10-inch ovenproof nonstick skillet over medium heat. Add potatoes and cook, covered, stirring occasionally until tender, 10 minutes. Add asparagus, leek, and thyme and cook, covered, until potatoes are tender and asparagus is crisp-tender, about 5 minutes more. Stir in ham and cook until heated through, 1 minute.

3 Whisk together egg whites, eggs, salt, and pepper in medium bowl. Pour egg mixture into skillet and spread evenly over vegetables. Reduce heat to medium-low and cook, without stirring, until edges are set, about 4 minutes.

4 Transfer skillet to oven and bake 12 minutes. Remove from oven and sprinkle frittata with goat cheese. Return to oven and bake until cheese is melted and frittata is set in center, about 3 minutes longer. Cut into 4 wedges.

4 **SmartPoints value per serving** (1 wedge): 210 Cal, 11 g Total Fat, 6 g Sat Fat, 719 mg Sod, 8 g Total Carb, 2 g Sugar, 2 g Fib, 19 g Prot.

Whole-grain mango muffins

Serves 12

¾   **cup all-purpose flour**

¾   **cup whole wheat flour**

¾   **cup firmly packed light brown sugar**

½   **cup old-fashioned oats**

¼   **cup wheat germ**

1½ **teaspoons cinnamon**

1½ **teaspoons baking powder**

½   **teaspoon ground ginger**

½   **teaspoon salt**

1   **cup low-fat buttermilk**

1   **large egg**

¼   **cup canola oil**

1   **teaspoon vanilla extract**

2   **mangoes, peeled, pitted, and diced**

1 Preheat oven to 400°F. Line 12 muffin cups with paper liners; spray liners with nonstick spray.

2 Combine all-purpose flour, whole wheat flour, brown sugar, oats, wheat germ, cinnamon, baking powder, ginger, and salt in medium bowl.

3 Whisk together buttermilk, egg, oil, and vanilla in small bowl. Add buttermilk mixture to flour mixture, stirring just until blended. Gently stir in mangoes.

4 Fill muffin cups evenly with batter. Bake until toothpick inserted in center of muffins comes out clean, 18–21 minutes. Cool in pan on wire rack 5 minutes. Remove muffins from pan and cool on rack. Serve warm or at room temperature.

 SmartPoints value per serving (1 muffin): 220 Cal, 6 g Total Fat, 1 g Sat Fat, 198 mg Sod, 39 g Total Carb, 22 g Sugar, 3 g Fib, 5 g Prot.

Tip

Mangoes are available year-round, but one of the best varieties, the juicy, jam-sweet Alphonso, is available from mid-April through May. Other excellent late-spring varieties to seek out are Haitian and Ataulfo.

Green breakfast smoothie

Serves 4

2 **cups lightly packed baby spinach**

1 **cup plain fat-free Greek yogurt**

1 **large navel or Valencia orange, peeled, sectioned, and seeded**

¼ **cup freshly squeezed orange juice**

1 **tablespoon honey**

2 **teaspoons minced peeled fresh ginger**

6 **ice cubes**

Combine spinach, yogurt, orange sections, orange juice, honey, ginger, and ice cubes in blender and puree. Pour into 4 glasses.

 SmartPoints value per serving (generous ⅔ cup): 82 Cal, 0 g Total Fat, 0 g Sat Fat, 33 mg Sod, 14 g Total Carb, 12 g Sugar, 2 g Fib, 7 g Prot.

Tip

Pre-washed greens, such as baby spinach, do not need to be rinsed again at home. They are treated with chlorinated water after picking to ensure safety.

Ginger breakfast cakes with quick strawberry jam

Serves 8

Cakes

1¼	**cups all-purpose flour**
½	**cup whole wheat flour**
3	**tablespoons sugar**
2	**teaspoons baking powder**
¼	**teaspoon salt**
⅓	**cup minced crystallized ginger**
⅓	**cup cold unsalted butter, cut into small pieces**
2	**large eggs**
⅓	**cup low-fat buttermilk**
1	**teaspoon vanilla extract**

Jam

1	**pound fresh strawberries, hulled and chopped**
3	**tablespoons sugar**
1	**tablespoon lemon juice**

1 Preheat oven to 400°F. Line large baking sheet with parchment paper.

2 Whisk together all-purpose and whole wheat flours, sugar, baking powder, and salt in medium bowl. Stir in ginger. With pastry blender, cut butter into flour mixture until butter is size of small peas.

3 Whisk together, eggs, buttermilk, and vanilla in small bowl. Add egg mixture to flour mixture and stir just until moistened; do not overmix.

4 Turn dough out onto prepared baking sheet. With floured hands, pat dough into 8-inch disk about 1½-inches thick. With floured knife, cut dough into 8 wedges (do not separate wedges). Bake until cakes just begin to brown, about 20 minutes.

5 Meanwhile to make jam, combine strawberries, sugar, and lemon juice in medium saucepan and set over medium heat. Cook, stirring occasionally, until sugar dissolves, 1–2 minutes.

6 Increase heat to medium-high. Cook, mashing strawberries with potato masher or back of wooden spoon, until jam is thickened and bubbling, about 10 minutes. Transfer to shallow bowl to cool slightly. Serve cakes with jam.

9 **SmartPoints value per serving** (1 cake and ¼ cup jam): 252 Cal, 10 g Total Fat, 5 g Sat Fat, 231 mg Sod, 37 g Total Carb, 15 g Sugar, 3 g Fib, 5 g Prot.

Tip
Strawberries are available year-round, but the ones you find at farmers' markets or pick-your-own farms in the spring have unbeatable flavor and rich red color. Store fresh strawberries in a single layer in a paper towel–lined container up to 4 days.

Ginger breakfast cakes with quick strawberry jam

**Spring garden
vegetable soup**

Spring garden vegetable soup

Serves 4

2	teaspoons olive oil
1	carrot, thinly sliced
1	celery stalk, thinly sliced
1	small fennel bulb, trimmed and chopped
½	sweet onion, chopped
3	garlic cloves, minced
4	cups reduced-sodium vegetable broth
1	cup cherry or grape tomatoes, halved
¾	teaspoon salt
¼	teaspoon coarsely ground black pepper
¼	pound asparagus, trimmed and cut into 2-inch lengths
¼	pound sugar snap peas, trimmed and cut in half
1	teaspoon grated lemon zest
2	tablespoons lemon juice
¼	cup shaved Parmesan cheese
1	tablespoon chopped fresh dill

1 Heat oil in large saucepan over medium-high heat. Add carrot, celery, fennel, onion, and garlic. Cook, stirring often, until vegetables are softened, 8 minutes.

2 Add broth, tomatoes, salt, and pepper and bring to boil. Add asparagus and peas. Reduce heat and simmer until asparagus and peas are bright green and crisp-tender, about 2 minutes. Remove from heat and stir in lemon zest and juice.

3 Ladle soup into 4 serving bowls. Sprinkle evenly with Parmesan and dill.

2 **SmartPoints value per serving** (2 cups soup and 1 tablespoon cheese): 108 Cal, 4 g Total Fat, 1 g Sat Fat, 790 mg Sod, 15 g Total Carb, 7 g Sugar, 4 g Fib, 4 g Prot.

Tip
Buy extra sugar snap peas when you shop for this recipe. They cook in about 2 minutes and make a delicious side dish when tossed with lemon juice and fresh dill or parsley.

Chilled mint-pea soup with lemon yogurt

Serves 4

1	teaspoon olive oil
3	scallions, chopped
3	cups fresh shelled green peas or thawed frozen baby peas
2	cups reduced-sodium vegetable broth
3	tablespoons chopped fresh mint
¼	teaspoon salt
¼	teaspoon freshly ground black pepper
½	cup plain low-fat Greek yogurt
½	teaspoon grated lemon zest

1 Heat oil in medium saucepan over medium heat. Add scallions and cook, stirring constantly, until softened, about 1 minute. Add peas and 1 cup of broth and bring to boil. Reduce heat and simmer, stirring occasionally, until peas are just tender and still bright green, about 3 minutes. Transfer to bowl and cool to room temperature.

2 Transfer pea mixture to blender. Add remaining 1 cup of broth, 1½ tablespoons of mint, the salt, and pepper and puree. Transfer to bowl; cover and refrigerate until chilled, at least 2 hours or up to 6 hours.

3 Stir together yogurt, remaining 1½ tablespoons of mint, and lemon zest in small bowl. Ladle soup into 4 serving bowls and top evenly with yogurt mixture.

1 **SmartPoints value per serving** (scant 1 cup soup and 2 tablespoons yogurt mixture): 126 Cal, 2 g Total Fat, 0 g Sat Fat, 265 mg Sod, 19 g Total Carb, 8 g Sugar, 7 g Fib, 9 g Prot.

Tip
To get 3 cups of fresh shelled green peas, you'll need about 3 pounds of fresh pea pods.

Bulgur salad with fennel, radish, and basil

Serves 4

1	**cup bulgur**
2	**cups water**
½	**teaspoon salt**
2	**teaspoons grated lemon zest**
3	**tablespoons lemon juice**
2	**tablespoons extra-virgin olive oil**
1	**garlic clove, minced**
½	**teaspoon black pepper**
6	**small radishes, thinly sliced**
3	**scallions, thinly sliced**
1	**fennel bulb, trimmed, halved lengthwise, and thinly sliced**
½	**cup chopped fresh basil**

1 Combine bulgur, water, and ¼ teaspoon of salt in medium saucepan. Bring to boil over high heat. Reduce heat and cover. Simmer until tender, about 10 minutes. Drain any excess water. Let cool to room temperature.

2 Whisk together lemon zest and juice, oil, garlic, remaining ¼ teaspoon salt, and the pepper in large bowl. Add bulgur, radishes, scallions, fennel, and basil. Toss gently to combine.

5 **SmartPoints value per serving** (1 cup): 208 Cal, 7 g Total Fat, 1 g Sat Fat, 334 mg Sod, 33 g Total Carb, 3 g Sugar, 7 g Fib, 6 g Prot.

Tip
Although available year-round, fresh radishes are one of the first vegetables harvested in early spring and are a harbinger of the season. Look for unusual varieties such as White Icicle, a long white radish, or French Breakfast, a slender red and white radish.

Watercress salad with grapefruit and papaya

Serves 4

3	**tablespoons white balsamic vinegar**
2	**tablespoons orange juice**
2	**tablespoons canola oil**
1	**small shallot, minced**
½	**teaspoon Dijon mustard**
½	**teaspoon ground coriander**
½	**teaspoon salt**
¼	**teaspoon black pepper**
4	**cups tightly packed watercress sprigs**
2	**pink grapefruit, peeled and cut into segments**
½	**papaya, peeled, seeded, and diced**
1	**small leek, cleaned and very thinly sliced, white and light green parts only**

1 Whisk together vinegar, orange juice, oil, shallot, mustard, coriander, salt, and pepper in small bowl.

2 Divide watercress evenly among 4 plates. Top with grapefruit, papaya, and leek. Drizzle evenly with vinaigrette.

3 **SmartPoints value per serving** (1¼ cups salad and 2 tablespoons vinaigrette): 161 Cal, 7 g Total Fat, 1 g Sat Fat, 327 mg Sod, 24 g Total Carb, 19 g Sugar, 3 g Fib, 2 g Prot.

Tip
Leeks taste like delicate onions and when very thinly sliced, as in this recipe, they can be eaten raw.

**Watercress salad
with grapefruit
and papaya**

**Fava bean
sandwiches**

Fava bean sandwiches

Serves 6

1½ **cups shelled peeled fresh fava beans or thawed frozen peeled fava beans**

⅓ **cup part-skim ricotta**

½ **teaspoon grated lemon zest**

2 **tablespoons lemon juice**

1 **tablespoon olive oil**

1 **garlic clove, chopped**

½ **teaspoon salt**

¼ **teaspoon black pepper**

¼ **cup loosely packed fresh basil leaves**

1 **teaspoon drained capers**

3 **light English muffins, split and lightly toasted**

2 **plum tomatoes, thinly sliced**

½ **cup baby salad greens**

6 **very thin slices Vidalia or other sweet onion**

1 Combine beans, ricotta, lemon zest and juice, oil, garlic, salt, and pepper in food processor and process until almost smooth. Add basil and capers; pulse several times until basil is finely chopped.

2 Spread fava-bean mixture evenly on cut sides of muffins. Top with tomatoes, salad greens, and onions. Serve immediately. (Note: to substitute frozen baby lima beans for fava beans, cook 1½ cups beans in boiling water until tender, 8–10 minutes. Drain, rinse under cold running water and procede with recipe.)

3 **SmartPoints value per serving** (1 open-face sandwich): 153 Cal, 4 g Total Fat, 1 g Sat Fat, 334 mg Sod, 25 g Total Carb, 3 g Sugar, 6 g Fib, 8 g Prot.

Tip
To shell and peel fava beans, split open the pod and remove the beans. Cook in boiling water 30 seconds, drain, and rinse under cold water. Squeeze each bean to remove the skin. To get 1½ cups of shelled peeled favas, you'll need 3 pounds of fresh fava pods.

Open-face prosciutto, avocado, and arugula sandwiches

Serves 4

1   **ripe avocado, halved, pitted, and peeled**

1   **tablespoon minced fresh chives**

¼   **teaspoon grated lemon zest**

2   **tablespoons lemon juice**

¼   **teaspoon salt**

¼   **teaspoon cracked black pepper**

4   **slices light whole-grain bread, toasted**

8   **thin slices prosciutto**

1½   **cups lightly packed baby arugula**

4   **radishes, thinly sliced**

2   **teaspoons extra-virgin olive oil**

1 Coarsely mash avocado in medium bowl. Add chives, lemon zest, 1 tablespoon of lemon juice, ⅛ teaspoon of salt, and ⅛ teaspoon of pepper and stir to combine.

2 Spread avocado mixture evenly on one side of each bread slice. Top each with 2 slices prosciutto.

3 Place arugula and radishes in medium bowl. Add oil, remaining 1 tablespoon lemon juice, remaining ⅛ teaspoon salt, and remaining ⅛ teaspoon pepper and toss gently to coat. Top sandwiches with arugula mixture.

(8) **SmartPoints value per serving** (1 open-face sandwich): 259 Cal, 17 g Total Fat, 4 g Sat Fat, 1,209 mg Sod, 16 g Total Carb, 2 g Sugar, 6 g Fib, 15 g Prot.

Tip
Flavorful baby arugula is a versatile green to keep on hand. Use it to add a peppery punch to sandwiches and salads but also as a great substitute for basil in pesto or for spinach in a dip.

Quinoa with fresh peas and mint

Serves 6

1¾ cups reduced-sodium
    vegetable broth

1   cup quinoa, rinsed

1   shallot, minced

1   cup fresh shelled green peas
    or thawed frozen baby peas

2   scallions, thinly sliced

1   tablespoon thinly sliced
    fresh mint

1   tablespoon extra-virgin olive oil

1   teaspoon balsamic vinegar

½   teaspoon salt

⅛   teaspoon coarsely ground
    black pepper

1 Bring broth to boil in medium saucepan. Add quinoa and shallot; reduce heat to low and simmer, covered, until quinoa is tender, about 15 minutes, adding peas during last 3 minutes of cooking time. Transfer to large bowl.

2 Add scallions, mint, oil, vinegar, salt, and pepper to quinoa mixture and toss gently to combine. Serve warm or at room temperature.

4 **SmartPoints value per serving** (⅔ cup): 154 Cal, 4 g Total Fat, 1 g Sat Fat, 257 mg Sod, 24 g Total Carb, 3 g Sugar, 4 g Fib, 6 g Prot.

Tip
To make an attractive and delicious spring dinner, spoon the quinoa onto serving plates and top each with a grilled salmon fillet for no additional SmartPoints.

Freekeh with roasted tomatoes and fava beans

Serves 8

1	**cup freekeh**
3	**cups water**
1	**teaspoon salt**
1½	**cups shelled peeled fresh fava beans, thawed frozen peeled fava beans, or baby lima beans (see tip on page 17 to prepare fresh favas)**
1	**pint cherry or grape tomatoes, halved**
2	**tablespoons olive oil**
2	**garlic cloves, minced**
1	**cup loosely packed fresh flat-leaf parsley leaves**
3	**tablespoons white-wine vinegar**
1	**teaspoon Dijon mustard**
¼	**teaspoon black pepper**
3	**scallions, thinly sliced**

1 Combine freekeh, water, and ½ teaspoon of salt in large saucepan and bring to boil. Reduce heat and simmer, covered, until tender, 20 minutes, adding fava beans during last 2 minutes of cooking time. Drain, transfer to medium bowl, and let cool slightly.

2 Meanwhile, preheat oven to 400°F. Line medium rimmed baking sheet with foil.

3 Place tomatoes, 1½ teaspoons of oil, and 1 garlic clove in medium bowl and toss to coat. Place in prepared baking sheet and bake until skins of tomatoes just begin to burst, 10 minutes.

4 Combine parsley, vinegar, remaining 1½ tablespoons oil, remaining 1 garlic clove, the mustard, remaining ½ teaspoon salt, and pepper in food processor and puree. Add parsley mixture, tomatoes, and scallions to freekeh and toss to combine. Serve warm or at room temperature.

3 **SmartPoints value per serving** (⅔ cup): 220 Cal, 5 g Total Fat, 1 g Sat Fat, 319 mg Sod, 34 g Total Carb, 3 g Sugar, 11 g Fib, 11 g Prot.

Tip
Freekeh (pronounced FREE-kuh) is made from grains of wheat that are harvested before they are mature, and then roasted to give them a nutty flavor. Look for freekeh in large supermarkets or specialty food stores.

Grilled chicken with couscous-mango salad

Serves 4

4   (5-ounce) skinless boneless chicken breasts
1   cup mango nectar
3   garlic cloves, minced
1½ teaspoons grated lime zest
2   tablespoons plus ¼ cup lime juice
1   teaspoon ground cumin
¾   teaspoon salt
½   teaspoon black pepper
1   cup whole wheat couscous
1   tablespoon olive oil
1   teaspoon sugar
½   teaspoon minced chipotles en adobo
¼   cup chopped fresh cilantro
2   cups loosely packed baby arugula
¼   red onion, thinly sliced
1   mango, peeled, pitted, and cubed

1 Place chicken, mango nectar, 2 garlic cloves, ½ teaspoon of lime zest, 2 tablespoons of lime juice, the cumin, ¼ teaspoon of salt, and ¼ teaspoon of pepper in large zip-close plastic bag. Squeeze out air and seal bag; turn to coat chicken. Refrigerate, turning bag occasionally, at least 1 hour or up to 4 hours.

2 Spray grill rack with nonstick spray. Preheat grill to medium-high or prepare medium-high fire.

3 Prepare couscous according to package directions. Transfer couscous to medium bowl and let cool to room temperature.

4 Remove chicken from marinade and discard marinade. Place chicken on grill rack and grill, turning often, until chicken is cooked through, 8–10 minutes.

5 Whisk together oil, sugar, chipotles, remaining 1 garlic clove, remaining 1 teaspoon grated lime zest, remaining ¼ cup lime juice, remaining ½ teaspoon salt, and remaining ¼ teaspoon pepper in large bowl. Stir in cilantro. Add couscous, arugula, onion, and mango and toss to coat. Serve chicken with salad.

8 **SmartPoints value per serving** (1 chicken breast and 1 ¾ cups salad): 460 Cal, 8 g Total Fat, 1 g Sat Fat, 516 mg Sod, 59 g Total Carb, 24 g Sugar, 8 g Fib, 39 g Prot.

Roasted chicken with artichokes and potatoes

Serves 6

1	(3½-pound) whole chicken
2	garlic cloves, minced
2	teaspoons minced fresh thyme
3	teaspoons grated lemon zest
1	teaspoon olive oil
¾	teaspoon salt
½	teaspoon black pepper
1½	pounds fingerling or baby potatoes, halved, or quartered if large
1	cup water
4	tablespoons lemon juice
1	pound baby artichokes

1 Preheat oven to 400°F.

2 Remove and discard giblets and any large pieces of fat from chicken. If desired, fold wing tips under first joint and tie legs together with kitchen string. Loosen skin from breast and drumsticks by easing fingers under skin and gently separating skin from meat.

3 Combine garlic, thyme, 1 teaspoon of lemon zest, oil, ½ teaspoon of salt, and the pepper in small bowl. Rub half of mixture under loosened skin and over breast and legs of chicken. Place chicken in large roasting pan.

4 Combine potatoes and remaining garlic mixture in medium bowl and toss to coat. Arrange potatoes around chicken.

5 Combine ½ cup of water and 2 tablespoons of lemon juice in large bowl. Pull tough outer leaves from artichokes and trim stem. Cut off about ½ inch of top of each artichoke. Cut each artichoke in half lengthwise and dip in lemon-water to prevent browning. Place artichoke halves around chicken and drizzle with remaining lemon-water (water keeps vegetables from burning until chicken releases its juices). Spray vegetables lightly with olive oil nonstick spray.

6 Roast chicken and vegetables, stirring vegetables twice and adding ¼ cup of water each time, until instant-read thermometer inserted into thigh (not touching bone) registers 165°F, about 1 hour and 20 minutes. Remove vegetables from pan when tender, after about 1 hour. Transfer vegetables to large bowl. Add remaining 2 tablespoons lemon juice, remaining 2 teaspoons lemon zest, and remaining ¼ teaspoon salt and toss to coat. Cover to keep warm.

7 Place chicken on platter, cover loosely with foil, and let stand 10 minutes before carving. Carve chicken and divide chicken and vegetables evenly among 6 plates. Remove skin before eating chicken.

5 SmartPoints value per serving (⅙ of chicken, 4 artichoke halves, and ¾ cup potatoes) 284 Cal, 5 g Total Fat, 1 g Sat Fat, 483 mg Sod, 27 g Total Carb, 2 g Sugar, 7 g Fib, 33 g Prot.

Tip
Baby artichokes are not a miniature variety of artichokes. They grow on the lower part of the plant where they naturally mature to a smaller size.

Roasted chicken with artichokes and potatoes

**Grilled chicken with
mint chimichurri**

Grilled chicken with mint chimichurri

Serves 4

1	**cup packed fresh mint leaves**
⅔	**cup loosely packed fresh flat-leaf parsley leaves**
3	**tablespoons white-wine vinegar**
1	**tablespoon olive oil**
1	**tablespoon water**
2	**garlic cloves, chopped**
¾	**teaspoon salt**
⅛	**teaspoon red pepper flakes**
4	**(5-ounce) skinless boneless chicken breasts**
½	**teaspoon ground cumin**
¼	**teaspoon black pepper**

1 Spray grill rack with nonstick spray. Preheat grill to medium-high or prepare medium-high fire.

2 Meanwhile, to make chimichurri, combine mint, parsley, vinegar, oil, water, garlic, ¼ teaspoon of salt, and the red pepper flakes in mini–food processor and puree.

3 Sprinkle chicken with cumin, remaining ½ teaspoon of salt, and the black pepper. Place chicken on grill rack and grill, turning once, until chicken is cooked through, 8–10 minutes. Serve with chimichurri.

1   **SmartPoints value per serving** (1 chicken breast and scant 2 tablespoons sauce): 213 Cal, 7 g Total Fat, 1 g Sat Fat, 509 mg Sod, 3 g Total Carb, 0 g Sugar, 2 g Fib, 32 g Prot.

Tip
Serve the chicken with a salad of baby arugula tossed with lemon juice and salt and pepper to taste.

Chutney chicken sliders

Serves 6

¾   cup mango chutney, large pieces chopped

2   scallions, thinly sliced

2   teaspoons hot sauce

2   teaspoons curry powder

¾   teaspoon salt

⅓   cup panko bread crumbs

1¼ pounds extra lean ground chicken breast or extra lean ground turkey breast

2   teaspoons canola oil

12 small (1 ounce) whole grain dinner rolls, split

1   cup loosely packed baby salad greens

1   Combine ⅓ cup of chutney, scallions, hot sauce, curry powder, and salt in medium bowl. Stir in panko. Add chicken and stir just until combined. Do not overmix.

2   Heat 1 teaspoon of oil in large nonstick skillet over medium heat. Drop half of chicken mixture by ¼-cup measures into skillet, about 2 inches apart. Press down with spatula to form 2½-inch diameter patties.

3   Cook, turning once, until patties are cooked through, about 8 minutes. Repeat with remaining 1 teaspoon oil and remaining chicken mixture. Brush cooked patties with remaining chutney and serve patties in rolls topped with salad greens.

10 **SmartPoints value per serving** (2 sliders): 380 Cal, 8 g Total Fat, 1 g Sat Fat, 823 mg Sod, 47 g Total Carb, 15 g Sugar, 3 g Fib, 27 g Prot.

Tip
To add some crunchy spice to the sliders, top them with peppery baby arugula and crispy cucumber slices.

**Chutney
chicken sliders**

Filets mignons with spring onion salsa verde

Serves 4

3 teaspoons olive oil

½ Vidalia or other sweet onion, thinly sliced

1 garlic clove, minced

⅛ teaspoon red pepper flakes

⅔ cup chopped fresh flat-leaf parsley

⅓ cup finely chopped fresh basil

1 tablespoon drained capers

½ teaspoon grated lemon zest

1 tablespoon lemon juice

¾ teaspoon salt

4 (4-ounce) lean filets mignons, trimmed

⅛ teaspoon coarsely ground black pepper

2 small radishes, very thinly sliced

1 Heat 2 teaspoons of oil in medium skillet over medium heat. Add onion, garlic, and red pepper flakes and cook, stirring constantly, until onion is crisp-tender, 2 minutes. Transfer to medium bowl and stir in parsley, basil, capers, lemon zest and juice, and ¼ teaspoon of salt. Transfer to bowl and cover to keep warm.

2 Wipe out skillet. Heat remaining 1 teaspoon of oil in same skillet over medium-high heat. Sprinkle steaks with remaining ½ teaspoon of salt and the black pepper. Add steaks to skillet and cook, turning once, until instant-read thermometer inserted into sides of steaks registers 145°F, 4–5 minutes. Serve steaks with onion mixture and top with sliced radishes.

4 **SmartPoints value per serving** (1 filet and 3 tablespoons salsa verde): 210 Cal, 10 g Total Fat, 3 g Sat Fat, 556 mg Sod, 3 g Total Carb, 1 g Sugar, 1 g Fib, 26 g Prot.

Tip
Vidalia onions are only grown in a small region surrounding Vidalia, Georgia. They are planted in autumn and harvesting begins in April. If you can't find them, use Oso Sweet, Walla Walla, or Maui.

Filets mignons
with spring onion
salsa verde

Spice-crusted roast
pork tenderloin with
watercress salad

Spice-crusted roast pork tenderloin with watercress salad

Serves 4

Pork

1	garlic clove, minced
2	teaspoons chili powder
1	teaspoon ground cumin
½	teaspoon ground coriander
¼	teaspoon salt
¼	teaspoon black pepper
1	(1-pound) lean pork tenderloin, trimmed
1	teaspoon olive oil

Salad

2	tablespoons orange juice
2	tablespoons lime juice
1	scallion, thinly sliced
1½	tablespoons canola oil
1	tablespoon lemon juice
1	teaspoon sugar
1	garlic clove, minced
¼	teaspoon salt
¼	teaspoon black pepper
6	cups loosely packed trimmed watercress sprigs
1	cup grape or cherry tomatoes, halved

1 Preheat oven to 425°F.

2 To make pork, combine garlic, chili powder, cumin, coriander, salt, and pepper in small bowl. Rub seasoning on all sides of tenderloin.

3 Heat oil in large ovenproof skillet over medium-high heat. Add tenderloin and cook, turning occasionally, until browned on all sides, about 8 minutes. Transfer skillet to oven and bake until instant-read thermometer inserted into center registers 145°F, 15–20 minutes. Let pork rest 5 minutes; then cut into 24 slices.

4 Meanwhile, to make dressing, whisk together orange juice, lime juice, scallion, oil, lemon juice, sugar, garlic, salt, and pepper in small bowl.

5 Arrange watercress and tomatoes on serving platter. Top with tenderloin slices; drizzle with dressing.

4 **SmartPoints value per serving** (6 slices pork, 1¼ cups salad, and 2 tablespoons dressing): 211 Cal, 9 g Total Fat, 1 g Sat Fat, 414 mg Sod, 7 g Total Carb, 3 g Sugar, 1 g Fib, 26 g Prot.

Lamb chops with cucumber-mint salad

Serves 4

2	teaspoons ground cumin
2	teaspoons ground coriander
½	teaspoon cinnamon
¼	teaspoon ground allspice
¼	teaspoon black pepper
2	teaspoons grated orange zest
1¼	teaspoons salt
4	(5-ounce) lean lamb shoulder chops, trimmed
¼	cup finely chopped fresh mint
3	tablespoons plain low-fat yogurt
4	teaspoons white-wine vinegar
2	teaspoons olive oil
2	cucumbers, thinly sliced

1 Spray ridged grill pan with nonstick spray and set over medium-high heat until hot.

2 Combine cumin, coriander, cinnamon, allspice, pepper, orange zest, and 1 teaspoon of salt in small bowl. Lightly spray lamb with olive oil nonstick spray. Rub seasoning all over lamb.

3 Place lamb in grill pan and cook, turning once, until instant-read thermometer inserted into centers of chops registers 145°F, about 8 minutes.

4 Meanwhile, stir together mint, yogurt, vinegar, oil, and remaining ¼ teaspoon salt in large bowl. Add cucumber and toss to combine. Serve lamb chops with cucumber salad.

5 **SmartPoints value per serving** (1 lamb chop and ¾ cup salad): 251 Cal, 11 g Total Fat, 3 g Sat Fat, 834 mg Sod, 6 g Total Carb, 3 g Sugar, 1 g Fib, 31 g Prot.

Tip
Instead of lamb, you can use skinless boneless chicken breasts or boneless pork chops in this recipe.

Indian-spiced lamb chops with fresh mint sauce

Serves 4

1   **cup lightly packed fresh mint leaves**

½   **cup lightly packed fresh cilantro leaves**

2   **tablespoons lemon juice**

1   **tablespoon water**

1   **serrano pepper, seeded and minced**

1   **garlic clove, minced**

1½   **teaspoons sugar**

1   **teaspoon grated peeled fresh ginger**

½   **teaspoon ground coriander**

½   **teaspoon ground cumin**

¼   **teaspoon ground ginger**

¼   **teaspoon salt**

¼   **teaspoon freshly ground black pepper**

1   **teaspoon olive oil**

4   **(4-ounce) lean bone-in lamb loin chops, trimmed**

1 To make sauce, combine mint, cilantro, lemon juice, water, serrano pepper, garlic, sugar, and fresh ginger in blender or food processor and puree. Set aside.

2 To make lamb, stir together coriander, cumin, ground ginger, salt, and black pepper in small bowl. Sprinkle mixture all over lamb, pressing so it adheres.

3 Heat oil in large skillet over medium-high heat. Add lamb. Cook, turning once, until instant-read thermometer inserted into center of each chop registers 145°F, about 6 minutes. Serve lamb with sauce.

(4)   **SmartPoints value per serving** (1 lamb chop and generous 1 tablespoon sauce): 190 Cal, 8 g Total Fat, 3 g Sat Fat, 227 mg Sod, 4 g Total Carb, 2 g Sugar, 1 g Fib, 24 g Prot.

Tip
Serve the lamb chops with the first baby potatoes of the season (3 ounces of steamed baby potatoes will increase the per-serving SmartPoints value by 2).

Grilled tuna with
cucumber-noodle salad

Grilled tuna with cucumber-noodle salad

Serves 4

3 tablespoons lime juice

2 tablespoons rice vinegar

1½ tablespoons sugar

1 teaspoon chili-garlic sauce

½ teaspoon salt

⅓ cup hot water

½ (8-ounce) package thin rice noodles

6 radishes, thinly sliced

½ English (seedless) cucumber, halved lengthwise and sliced

¼ red onion, thinly sliced

¼ cup loosely packed fresh cilantro leaves plus additional for garnish

4 (5-ounce) tuna steaks

1 teaspoon olive oil

½ teaspoon black pepper

Lime wedges

1 Combine lime juice, vinegar, sugar, chili-garlic sauce, and ¼ teaspoon of salt in medium bowl. Add hot water and stir until sugar dissolves. Set aside to cool.

2 Meanwhile, cook rice noodles according to package directions. Rinse with cold water and drain. Add to lime juice mixture. Add radishes, cucumber, onion, and cilantro and toss to combine.

3 Heat ridged grill pan over medium-high heat. Brush tuna on all sides with oil. Sprinkle with remaining ¼ teaspoon salt and the pepper. Place in pan and cook, turning once, 6 minutes for rare, or to desired doneness. Cut steaks across grain into ¼-inch-thick slices. Divide noodle salad among 4 plates. Top evenly with tuna and garnish with cilantro leaves. Serve with lime wedges.

5 **SmartPoints value per serving** (1 tuna steak and 1¼ cups noodle salad): 302 Cal, 2 g Total Fat, 0 g Sat Fat, 410 mg Sod, 33 g Total Carb, 6 g Sugar, 2 g Fib, 36 g Prot.

Tip
English and Persian cucumbers are thin-skinned and have few seeds. Their skin is not bitter and has no waxy coating, so you can eat the peel. English cucumbers are about a foot long but Persian cukes are only about 5 inches long.

Arctic char with tarragon leeks

Serves 4

2 teaspoons olive oil

2 leeks, cut crosswise into thirds, cleaned and thinly sliced lengthwise, white and light green parts only

2 shallots, minced

¾ teaspoon salt

¼ teaspoon coarsely ground black pepper

½ cup reduced-sodium chicken broth

1 tablespoon chopped fresh tarragon

2 teaspoons chopped fresh flat-leaf parsley

4 (5-ounce) arctic char fillets

Lemon wedges

1 Heat 1 teaspoon of oil in large nonstick skillet over medium heat. Add leeks, shallots, ¼ teaspoon of salt, and ⅛ teaspoon of pepper. Cook, stirring often until softened, 2 minutes.

2 Add broth and tarragon. Reduce heat to low, and simmer, covered, until leeks are tender, 4 minutes. Uncover and cook until liquid evaporates, about 1 minute more. Remove from heat and stir in parsley.

3 Meanwhile, sprinkle arctic char with remaining ½ teaspoon of salt and remaining ⅛ teaspoon of pepper.

4 Heat remaining 1 teaspoon oil in large skillet over medium-high heat. Add char and cook, turning once, just until opaque in center, about 10 minutes. Serve fish topped with leek mixture. Serve with lemon wedges.

1 **SmartPoints value per serving** (1 fillet and ¼ cup leek mixture): 209 Cal, 6 g Total Fat, 1 g Sat Fat, 603 mg Sod, 10 g Total Carb, 3 g Sugar, 2 g Fib, 29 g Prot.

Tip
Arctic char is closely related to salmon and trout. Its pinkish color resembles that of salmon, and it has a clean, mild flavor. If you can't find arctic char, you can substitute salmon in this recipe.

Arctic char with tarragon leeks

**Pasta and spring
vegetables with feta**

Pasta and spring vegetables with feta

Serves 6

½   **pound whole wheat penne or fusilli**

1½   **cups shelled peeled fresh fava beans, thawed frozen peeled fava beans, or baby lima beans (see tip on page 17 to prepare fresh favas)**

½   **pound asparagus, cut into 1½-inch lengths**

1   **pint grape or cherry tomatoes, halved**

¼   **cup chopped fresh flat-leaf parsley**

2   **tablespoons thinly sliced fresh mint**

2   **tablespoons extra-virgin olive oil**

½   **teaspoon grated lemon zest**

2   **tablespoons lemon juice**

2   **garlic cloves, minced**

½   **teaspoon salt**

¼   **teaspoon black pepper**

¼   **cup crumbled feta cheese**

Fresh mint sprigs (optional)

1 Cook pasta according to package directions, adding fava beans and asparagus during last 2 minutes of cooking time. Drain and rinse under cold running water. Drain again.

2 Meanwhile, combine tomatoes, parsley, mint, oil, lemon zest and juice, garlic, salt, and pepper in large bowl. Add pasta mixture and toss to coat. Sprinkle with feta. Garnish with mint sprigs, if desired.

6   **SmartPoints value per serving** (1 cup): 337 Cal, 7 g Total Fat, 2 g Sat Fat, 279 mg Sod, 55 g Total Carb, 4 g Sugar, 15 g Fib, 18 g Prot.

Tip
You can use fresh peppermint or spearmint in this recipe, though spearmint will give the dish a more delicate flavor. If you don't care for mint, use fresh basil or cilantro instead.

Goat cheese polenta with spring vegetables

Serves 4

1	teaspoon olive oil
3	garlic cloves, minced
½	pound sugar snap peas, trimmed
½	pound asparagus, trimmed and cut into 2-inch lengths
1	cup baby carrots, halved lengthwise
2	tablespoons water
½	teaspoon salt
¼	teaspoon freshly ground black pepper
¼	teaspoon grated lemon zest
1	tablespoon lemon juice
4	cups reduced-sodium vegetable broth
1	cup quick-cooking polenta
4	ounces crumbled goat cheese (1 cup)
1	tablespoon minced fresh chives

1 Heat oil in large nonstick skillet and set over medium heat. Add garlic and cook, stirring constantly, until fragrant, 30 seconds. Add peas, asparagus, carrots, water, salt, and pepper. Cook, covered, stirring occasionally, until vegetables are crisp-tender, about 5 minutes. Stir in lemon zest and juice. Remove from heat, cover, and keep warm.

2 Bring broth to boil in medium saucepan. Gradually sprinkle polenta into broth, whisking constantly. Reduce heat and cook, continuing to whisk, until thick and creamy, 3–4 minutes. Remove from heat and stir in ½ cup of goat cheese.

3 Divide polenta evenly among 4 bowls and top with vegetable mixture. Sprinkle evenly with remaining ½ cup of goat cheese and the chives.

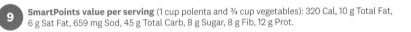

9 **SmartPoints value per serving** (1 cup polenta and ¾ cup vegetables): 320 Cal, 10 g Total Fat, 6 g Sat Fat, 659 mg Sod, 45 g Total Carb, 8 g Sugar, 8 g Fib, 12 g Prot.

Singapore noodles with tofu and vegetables

Serves 4

5   ounces fine brown rice noodles

3   tablespoons water

2   tablespoons Asian fish sauce

2   tablespoons rice vinegar

1   tablespoon hoisin sauce

2   teaspoons curry powder

2   teaspoons tomato paste

3   teaspoons canola oil

8   ounces firm tofu, cut into ½-inch cubes

1   pound asparagus, trimmed and cut into 1½-inch lengths

6   ounces sugar snap peas, trimmed and halved crosswise

6   thin scallions, thinly sliced

1½ tablespoons minced peeled fresh ginger

½   cup chopped fresh cilantro

Lime wedges

1 Boil rice noodles according to package directions.

2 Meanwhile, stir together water, fish sauce, vinegar, hoisin sauce, curry powder, and tomato paste in small bowl.

3 Heat large deep skillet or wok over high heat until drop of water sizzles in pan. Add 2 teaspoons of oil and swirl to coat pan. Add tofu and stir-fry until lightly browned, about 3 minutes. Transfer to plate. Add remaining 1 teaspoon of oil to pan. Add asparagus and stir-fry 2 minutes. Add peas, scallions, and ginger and stir-fry until vegetables are crisp-tender, about 2 minutes.

4 Add noodles and fish sauce mixture to pan and stir-fry until noodles are heated through, about 1 minute. Divide evenly among 4 plates, sprinkle with cilantro, and serve with lime wedges.

5 **SmartPoints value per serving** (2 cups): 269 Cal, 7 g Total Fat, 1 g Sat Fat, 872 mg Sod, 44 g Total Carb, 7 g Sugar, 6 g Fib, 12 g Prot.

Tip
To trim sugar snap peas, grasp the stem at the top of each pod and pull off the tough string that runs on the inside curve of the pea. Once you get the hang of it, it takes just a couple minutes to trim a pile of peas.

Penne primavera

Serves 4

½   **pound whole wheat penne**

2   **teaspoons olive oil**

½   **pound asparagus, trimmed and cut into 1-inch pieces**

2   **zucchini, cut into matchstick strips**

2   **(4-ounce) packages assorted fresh wild mushrooms (such as oyster, crimini, and shiitake), sliced (remove stems if using shiitakes)**

1   **cup shelled fresh peas or frozen green peas**

¾   **teaspoon salt**

¼   **teaspoon black pepper**

2   **ounces goat cheese, crumbled**

¼   **cup snipped fresh chives**

2   **tablespoons grated Pecorino cheese**

1 Cook pasta according to package instructions. Drain and reserve about ¼ cup of cooking liquid.

2 Meanwhile, heat oil in large skillet over medium-high heat. Add asparagus, zucchini, mushrooms, peas, salt, and pepper. Cook, stirring occasionally, until vegetables are crisp-tender, about 5 minutes.

3 Remove skillet from heat and add pasta. Stir in goat cheese, chives, and Pecorino. Add reserved cooking liquid 1 tablespoon at a time until sauce is creamy. Divide pasta among 4 plates.

8 **SmartPoints value per serving** (1½ cups pasta mixture and 1½ teaspoons cheese): 329 Cal, 7 g Total Fat, 2 g Sat Fat, 516 mg Sod, 55 g Total Carb, 7 g Sugar, 10 g Fib, 16 g Prot.

Warm chai rice pudding with mango

Serves 8

2   **cups fat-free milk**

1   **(13-ounce) can light (low-fat) coconut milk**

1   **cup jasmine or long-grain white rice**

⅓   **cup packed light brown sugar**

¼   **teaspoon salt**

1   **teaspoon vanilla extract**

¼   **teaspoon ground cardamom**

¼   **teaspoon cinnamon**

¼   **teaspoon ground ginger**

⅛   **teaspoon ground cloves**

2   **cups diced mango**

1 Stir together milk, coconut milk, rice, brown sugar, and salt in medium saucepan. Bring to boil over medium-high heat. Reduce heat to low and simmer, uncovered, stirring frequently, until rice is tender, about 20 minutes.

2 Remove from heat; stir in vanilla, cardamom, cinnamon, ginger, and cloves. Let stand at room temperature to cool slightly. Serve pudding warm, or cover and refrigerate until chilled, about 2 hours. Serve topped evenly with mango.

7 **SmartPoints value per serving** (scant ½ cup pudding and ¼ cup mango): 198 Cal, 3 g Total Fat, 2 g Sat Fat, 109 mg Sod, 38 g Total Carb, 18 g Sugar, 1 g Fib, 4 g Prot.

Tip
Stirring rice while it cooks is usually not recommended because it releases starch, preventing the rice from being fluffy. In this recipe, however, stirring helps create the soft creamy texture that makes rice pudding so comforting.

Lemon angel food cake with strawberry-balsamic compote

Serves 16

Cake

1	**cup sugar**
2	**teaspoons grated lemon zest**
12	**large egg whites, at room temperature**
¼	**teaspoon salt**
1	**tablespoon lemon juice**
1	**teaspoon vanilla extract**
¾	**teaspoon cream of tartar**
1	**cup cake flour**

Compote

1½	**pounds fresh strawberries, hulled and quartered**
1	**tablespoon sugar**
1	**tablespoon balsamic glaze**

1 To make cake, preheat oven to 350°F.

2 Stir together sugar and lemon zest in small bowl. With electric mixer on medium speed, beat egg whites and salt in large bowl until foamy. Beat in lemon juice and vanilla. Add cream of tartar; beat until soft peaks form. Add sugar mixture a few tablespoons at a time to egg white mixture, beating until stiff peaks form. (Lemon zest sticks to beaters, so be sure to scrape them well before adding flour.)

3 Fold in flour with rubber spatula ¼ cup at a time. (Be careful not to overmix.)

4 Pour batter into ungreased 10-inch tube pan, spreading evenly. Bake until cake springs back when lightly pressed, 20–25 minutes. Invert pan onto its legs or neck of bottle and let cool completely.

5 Run thin knife around edge of cake to loosen it from side and center tube of pan. Remove cake from pan and put on serving plate.

6 To make compote, combine ½ pound of strawberries and sugar in large bowl; coarsely crush with large spoon or potato masher. Stir in remaining strawberries and balsamic glaze.

7 Cut cake into 16 slices and place on plates. Spoon compote evenly over each slice.

 SmartPoints value per serving (¹⁄₁₆ of cake and ¼ cup compote): 112 Cal, 0 g Total Fat, 0 g Sat Fat, 78 mg Sod, 24 g Total Carb, 16 g Sugar, 1 g Fib, 4 g Prot.

Lemon angel food cake with strawberry-balsamic compote

**Rhubarb-strawberry
shortcakes**

Rhubarb-strawberry shortcakes

Serves 12

2   cups sliced fresh rhubarb or thawed frozen sliced rhubarb

3   tablespoons plus ¼ cup sugar

2   tablespoons water

1   pound fresh strawberries, hulled and sliced

1½   cups white whole wheat flour

1½   teaspoons baking powder

¼   teaspoon salt

4   tablespoons unsalted butter, cut into pieces

⅔   cup low-fat buttermilk

1   large egg

½   teaspoon grated lemon zest

¾   cup thawed frozen fat-free whipped topping

1 Combine rhubarb, 3 tablespoons of sugar, and water in medium saucepan. Bring to boil, reduce heat to medium-low, and cook, stirring occasionally, until rhubarb is tender, 5 minutes. Stir in strawberries and cook, stirring often, until softened, 3 minutes. Transfer to bowl to cool. Refrigerate, covered, until chilled, 2 hours or up to 2 days.

2 Preheat oven to 425°F. Line large baking sheet with parchment paper.

3 Whisk together flour, remaining ¼ cup of sugar, the baking powder, and salt in large bowl. With pastry blender or 2 knives used scissor-fashion, cut in butter until mixture resembles coarse crumbs.

4 Whisk together buttermilk, egg, and grated lemon zest in small bowl. Add buttermilk mixture to flour mixture, stirring gently just until soft dough forms (dough will appear wet).

5 Turn dough onto well-floured work surface. Press dough together and pat to ½-inch thickness. With floured 2-inch round cutter, cut out biscuits without twisting cutter. Gather scraps and reroll, making total of 12 biscuits. Place biscuits on prepared baking sheet.

6 Bake until golden brown, 15–17 minutes. Transfer to wire rack to cool.

7 Split biscuits in half horizontally. Place bottoms on 12 plates and top each with generous ¼ cup of rhubarb mixture. Cover with tops of biscuits. Top each with 1 tablespoon of whipped topping. Serve immediately.

6 **SmartPoints value per serving** (1 biscuit, ¼ cup compote, and 1 tablespoon topping): 155 Cal, 5 g Total Fat, 3 g Sat Fat, 134 mg Sod, 24 g Total Carb, 12 g Sugar, 1 g Fib, 4 g Prot.

Chocolate berry pavlova

Serves 12

¾ cup plus 1½ tablespoons granulated sugar

¼ cup packed light brown sugar

¼ cup unsweetened cocoa, sifted

4 large egg whites, at room temperature

¼ teaspoon cream of tartar

⅛ teaspoon salt

½ cup mascarpone cheese

4 ounces light cream cheese (Neufchâtel), softened

1 tablespoon low-fat (1%) milk

½ teaspoon vanilla extract

½ pound fresh strawberries, hulled and sliced

1 ounce bittersweet chocolate

1 Preheat oven to 250°F. Line large baking sheet with parchment paper.

2 Whisk together ¾ cup of granulated sugar, brown sugar, and cocoa in medium bowl. With electric mixer on medium speed, beat egg whites, cream of tartar, and salt in large bowl until soft peaks form. Add sugar mixture 2 tablespoons at a time, beating until stiff, glossy peaks form.

3 Spoon onto prepared baking sheet and spread meringue into 8-inch circle to make "nest" with 1-inch-high edge. Bake 1½ hours. Turn oven off, and let cool in oven 2 hours. Remove from oven and cool completely on wire rack.

4 With electric mixer on medium speed, beat mascarpone, cream cheese, milk, remaining 1½ tablespoons of granulated sugar, and vanilla in medium bowl until smooth. Spoon into center of meringue and spread evenly. Top with strawberries. Using vegetable peeler, shave chocolate over berries. Cut into 12 wedges and serve immediately.

8 **SmartPoints value per serving** (1 slice): 160 Cal, 7 g Total Fat, 5 g Sat Fat, 94 mg Sod, 23 g Total Carb, 20 g Sugar, 1 g Fib, 3 g Prot.

Chocolate berry
pavlova

Greek yogurt with rhubarb-raspberry spoon fruit

Serves 12

½   **cup water**

¼   **cup granulated sugar**

¼   **cup packed light brown sugar**

1   **pound fresh rhubarb, trimmed and thinly sliced, or 1 (10-ounce) box frozen sliced rhubarb, thawed**

6   **ounces fresh raspberries**

6   **cups plain fat-free Greek yogurt**

6   **tablespoons toasted sliced almonds**

1 Combine water, granulated sugar, and brown sugar in medium saucepan and set over medium-high heat. Cook, stirring frequently, until sugar dissolves, about 2 minutes.

2 Add rhubarb and cook, stirring often, until just tender, 5–7 minutes. Add raspberries and cook, stirring often, until berries just begin to fall apart, about 3 minutes. Transfer to bowl and cool to room temperature. (The sauce may be made up to 4 days ahead and stored in a covered container in refrigerator.)

3 For each serving, place ½ cup yogurt into bowl. Top with 2 tablespoons sauce and ½ tablespoon almonds.

3   **SmartPoints value per serving** (1 dessert): 129 Cal, 2 g Total Fat, 0 g Sat Fat, 44 mg Sod, 16 g Total Carb, 13 g Sugar, 2 g Fib, 13 g Prot.

Tip

Ruby red rhubarb stalks are botanically a vegetable, but it is used as a fruit to make desserts, jams, and sauces.

Strawberry-mandarin granita

Serves 6

1 **pound fresh ripe strawberries, hulled and coarsely chopped**

½ **teaspoon grated mandarin orange zest or tangerine zest**

3 **mandarin oranges or tangerines, peeled, seeded, and sectioned**

⅓ **cup sugar**

1 **tablespoon lemon juice**

Fresh mint sprigs (optional)

1 Combine strawberries, orange zest, orange segments, sugar, and lemon juice in blender and puree. Pour into 8-inch baking dish. Cover with foil and freeze until partially frozen, about 1½ hours.

2 With fork, scrape frozen outer edges toward center of dish. Cover and freeze until mixture is completely frozen, scraping with fork every 30 minutes, about 3 hours.

3 Remove granita from freezer; let stand at room temperature 5 minutes. Scrape granita with fork until light and fluffy. Spoon evenly into 6 dessert dishes and garnish with mint sprigs if desired. Granita can be frozen up to 1 week.

3 **SmartPoints value per serving** (½ cup): 91 Cal, 0 g Total Fat, 0 g Sat Fat, 2 mg Sod, 23 g Total Carb, 20 g Sugar, 2 g Fib, 1 g Prot.

Cherries

↑ Apricots

Cantaloupes →

Cayenne
pepper

Tomatillos

Eggplant

Shelling
beans

Blackberries

Chapter 2
Summer
Let a stroll through the farmers' market inspire fresh, simple meals.

Kohlrabi

Basil

Tomatoes

Blueberries

Wax beans

In this chapter

What's in season

- Apricots
- Basil
- Bell peppers
- Bibb lettuce
- Blackberries
- Blueberries
- Carrots
- Cherries
- Chile peppers
- Corn
- Cucumbers
- Eggplant
- Green beans
- Melons
- Napa cabbage
- Nectarines
- Peaches
- Plums
- Raspberries
- Romaine lettuce
- Snow peas
- Tomatoes
- Watermelon
- Yellow summer squash
- Zucchini

Scrambled egg, goat cheese, and tomato sandwiches

Serves 4

6	**large eggs**
½	**teaspoon salt**
⅛	**teaspoon black pepper**
2	**teaspoons canola oil**
2	**ounces goat cheese, crumbled**
2	**light whole-grain English muffins, split and toasted**
4	**(½-inch) slices of large tomato**
2	**tablespoons chopped fresh basil**

1 Whisk together eggs, salt, and pepper in medium bowl.

2 Heat oil in large nonstick skillet over medium-low heat. Add egg mixture to skillet and cook, stirring gently, 2 minutes. Add goat cheese and continue to cook and stir, until eggs are set but still moist, 1 minute longer.

3 Divide English muffin halves among 4 plates. Top each with tomato slice and then with eggs. Sprinkle with basil and serve at once.

4 **SmartPoints value per serving** (1 open-face sandwich): 221 Cal, 13 g Total Fat, 5 g Sat Fat, 560 mg Sod, 12 g Total Carb, 2 g Sugar, 2 g Fib, 15 g Prot.

Skillet ratatouille with eggs

Serves 4

2	teaspoons olive oil
1	small red onion, finely chopped
2	garlic cloves, minced
1	small yellow or red bell pepper, diced
1	zucchini, diced
1	large tomato, chopped
½	eggplant, diced
2	tablespoons tomato paste
¾	teaspoon salt
½	teaspoon herbes de Provence
¼	cup kalamata olives, pitted and chopped
¼	cup plus 2 tablespoons torn fresh basil
1	tablespoon balsamic vinegar
4	large eggs
¼	cup crumbled feta cheese

1 Heat oil in large nonstick skillet over medium heat. Add onion and garlic and cook, stirring often, until onion begins to soften, 3 minutes. Add bell pepper, zucchini, tomato, eggplant, tomato paste, salt, and herbes de Provence and cook, stirring often, until vegetables are tender, about 10 minutes. Stir in olives, ¼ cup of basil, and vinegar.

2 With back of spoon, make 4 indentations in vegetable mixture. Crack 1 egg into each indentation. Reduce heat to low, and cook, covered, until egg whites are opaque and yolks are set, about 5 minutes. Sprinkle with feta and remaining 2 tablespoons basil and serve at once.

3 **SmartPoints value per serving** (scant 1 cup vegetables with 1 egg): 180 Cal, 11 g Total Fat, 3 g Sat Fat, 736 mg Sod, 14 g Total Carb, 7 g Sugar, 4 g Fib, 10 g Prot.

**Skillet ratatouille
with eggs**

Summer vegetable frittata

Serves 4

4   **large eggs**
4   **large egg whites**
2   **tablespoons fat-free milk**
¾   **teaspoon salt**
¼   **teaspoon black pepper**
2   **teaspoons olive oil**
½   **small red onion, finely chopped**
1   **garlic clove, minced**
1   **red bell pepper, diced**
¼   **pound green beans, trimmed and cut into ¼-inch pieces**
1   **small tomato, chopped**
½   **cup fresh corn kernels (from 1 ear) or frozen corn kernels**
1   **tablespoon finely chopped fresh basil**

1 Preheat oven to 375°F.

2 Whisk together eggs, egg whites, milk, ¼ teaspoon of salt, and ⅛ teaspoon of black pepper in medium bowl.

3 Heat oil in 10-inch ovenproof nonstick skillet over medium heat. Add onion and garlic and cook, stirring occasionally, until onion begins to soften, 3 minutes.

4 Add bell pepper and green beans and cook, stirring occasionally, until softened, about 3 minutes. Add tomato, corn, remaining ½ teaspoon salt, and remaining ⅛ teaspoon black pepper and cook, stirring occasionally, 2 minutes. Spread vegetables evenly in skillet.

5 Pour egg mixture into skillet and spread evenly over vegetables. Reduce heat to medium-low and cook until edges set, about 4 minutes. Transfer skillet to oven and bake just until set in center, 15 minutes.

6 Sprinkle frittata with basil. Cut into 4 wedges.

1   **SmartPoints value per serving** (1 wedge): 149 Cal, 7 g Total Fat, 2 g Sat Fat, 570 mg Sod, 10 g Total Carb, 4 g Sugar, 2 g Fib, 12 g Prot.

Blueberry-almond muesli

Serves 4

¾ cup plain unsweetened almond milk

⅓ cup plain fat-free Greek yogurt

1 tablespoon orange juice

1 teaspoon honey

½ teaspoon vanilla extract

Drop almond extract

½ teaspoon cinnamon

⅛ teaspoon salt

1 cup old-fashioned oats

8 pitted dates, finely chopped

1 cup fresh blueberries

¼ cup toasted slivered almonds

1 Whisk together almond milk, yogurt, orange juice, honey, vanilla, almond extract, cinnamon, and salt in medium bowl. Stir in oats and dates. Cover and refrigerate overnight.

2 Spoon muesli evenly into 4 bowls. Top evenly with blueberries and almonds and serve at once.

7 **SmartPoints value per serving** (about ½ cup): 214 Cal, 5 g Total Fat, 1 g Sat Fat, 107 mg Sod, 36 g Total Carb, 17 g Sugar, 5 g Fib, 8 g Prot.

Tip
Blueberries and finely chopped dried dates lend natural sweetness to the muesli. Depending on what's fresh at your market, top the cereal with berries in spring and summer and in autumn and winter, try orange segments or chopped apple.

Cinnamon French toast with raspberries

Cinnamon French toast with raspberries

Serves 6

2   **large egg whites**
1   **large egg**
⅓   **cup low-fat (1%) milk**
2   **tablespoons light brown sugar**
½   **teaspoon cinnamon**
½   **teaspoon vanilla extract**
6   **slices light whole wheat sandwich bread**
1½ **teaspoons canola oil**
3   **cups fresh raspberries**
1½ **teaspoons confectioners' sugar**

1 Whisk together egg whites, egg, milk, brown sugar, cinnamon, and vanilla in large shallow dish.

2 Dip each slice of bread in egg mixture, turning several times to coat.

3 Heat ½ teaspoon of oil in large nonstick skillet over medium heat. Add 2 slices of bread and cook, turning once, until golden brown, about 6 minutes. Repeat with remaining ½ teaspoon oil and remaining bread. Cut each slice in half on diagonal. Top with raspberries and sprinkle with confectioners' sugar.

3 **SmartPoints value per serving** (1 slice toast, ½ cup raspberries, and ¼ teaspoon sugar): 127 Cal, 3 g Total Fat, 1 g Sat Fat, 108 mg Sod, 21 g Total Carb, 8 g Sugar, 6 g Fib, 6 g Prot.

Greek yogurt with cherry compote and pistachios

Serves 4

1⅓ cups fresh sweet cherries, pitted and halved, or unsweetened frozen pitted cherries, halved

½ cup orange juice

2 teaspoons honey

1 (3-inch) cinnamon stick

¼ teaspoon salt

2 cups plain fat-free Greek yogurt

2 tablespoons finely chopped toasted pistachios

1 To make compote, combine cherries, orange juice, honey, cinnamon stick, and salt in small saucepan and bring to boil over medium heat. Reduce heat to medium-low and simmer, stirring occasionally, until cherries soften and liquid begins to thicken slightly, about 12 minutes.

2 Transfer to medium bowl; remove and discard cinnamon stick. Let stand to cool to room temperature. Serve at room temperature or transfer to airtight container and refrigerate until chilled, at least 2 hours or up to 4 days.

3 To serve, divide yogurt evenly among 4 bowls. Top evenly with compote and sprinkle evenly with pistachios.

2 **SmartPoints value per serving** (1 bowl): 139 Cal, 2 g Total Fat, 0 g Sat Fat, 187 mg Sod, 18 g Total Carb, 14 g Sugar, 2 g Fib, 13 g Prot.

Tip
Choose sweet cherries for this recipe. They are naturally sweet enough to eat on their own. Sour cherries will make your mouth pucker unless they are prepared with a generous amount of sugar.

Greek yogurt with
cherry compote
and pistachios

Raspberry-peach
smoothies

Raspberry-peach smoothies

Serves 4

2   ripe peaches, peeled, pitted, and sliced

2   (6-ounce) packages fresh raspberries or 2¾ cups frozen unsweetened raspberries

1½ cups plain fat-free Greek yogurt

½   cup fat-free milk

1   tablespoon honey

3   ice cubes

Combine peaches, raspberries, yogurt, milk, honey, and ice cubes in blender and puree. Pour into 4 glasses and serve.

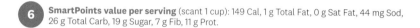

6   **SmartPoints value per serving** (scant 1 cup): 149 Cal, 1 g Total Fat, 0 g Sat Fat, 44 mg Sod, 26 g Total Carb, 19 g Sugar, 7 g Fib, 11 g Prot.

Tip

Instead of peaches, you can use nectarines and try blackberries or blueberries instead of raspberries.

Greek yogurt with warm blueberry sauce

Serves 6

2   **cups fresh blueberries**
2   **tablespoons sugar**
2   **tablespoons water**
½   **teaspoon grated lemon zest**
½   **teaspoon fresh lemon juice**
Pinch salt
3   **cups plain fat-free plain Greek yogurt**

1 Combine blueberries, sugar, and water in medium saucepan; set over medium-high heat and bring to boil. Reduce heat and simmer, stirring occasionally, until most blueberries burst and sauce is slightly thickened, 5–7 minutes.

2 Transfer sauce to medium bowl and stir in lemon zest, lemon juice, and salt. Let cool slightly. (Sauce can be made up to 4 days ahead and stored in a covered container in refrigerator.)

3 Spoon yogurt evenly into bowls; top with sauce and swirl sauce into yogurt.

1 **SmartPoints value per serving** (½ cup yogurt and about ¼ cup sauce): 111 Cal, 1 g Total Fat, 0 g Sat Fat, 89 mg Sod, 15 g Total Carb, 13 g Sugar, 1 g Fib, 12 g Prot.

Late-summer southwest turkey and vegetable soup

Serves 6

2	teaspoons canola oil
1	large onion, chopped
1	pound 93% lean ground turkey
4	teaspoons hot chili powder
2	teaspoons ground cumin
1½	teaspoons dried oregano
¾	teaspoon salt
4	cups reduced-sodium chicken broth
1	zucchini, quartered lengthwise and sliced
3	plum tomatoes, diced
1	cup fresh corn kernels (from 2 ears)
1	(15-ounce) can small white beans, rinsed and drained
½	cup chopped fresh cilantro
2	tablespoons fresh lime juice
Lime wedges	

1 Heat oil in Dutch oven over medium heat. Add onion and cook, stirring often, 3 minutes. Add turkey, chili powder, cumin, oregano, and salt and cook, breaking up turkey with spoon, until no longer pink, 6 minutes.

2 Add broth and bring to simmer. Add zucchini and tomatoes and simmer 4 minutes. Stir in corn and beans and cook until heated through, about 2 minutes. Remove from heat and stir in cilantro and lime juice. Serve with lime wedges.

3 **SmartPoints value per serving** (1½ cups): 267 Cal, 9 g Total Fat, 2 g Sat Fat, 1,007 mg Sod, 28 g Total Carb, 4 g Sugar, 6 g Fib, 22 g Prot.

Tip
If you don't have hot chili powder, substitute an equal amount of regular chili powder and add ⅛ teaspoon cayenne.

Blender gazpacho with avocado

Serves 4

2	**cups tomato-vegetable juice**
1	**large tomato, chopped**
½	**large red bell pepper, chopped**
¼	**English (seedless) cucumber, peeled and chopped**
½	**small red onion, chopped**
¼	**cup whole fresh cilantro leaves**
2	**garlic cloves, chopped**
1	**tablespoon chopped jalapeño pepper (leave in seeds for extra heat)**
2	**tablespoons white balsamic vinegar**
1	**tablespoon olive oil**
1	**tablespoon lime juice**
¾	**teaspoon salt**
¼	**teaspoon black pepper**
½	**avocado, pitted, peeled, and diced**

1 Combine all ingredients except avocado in blender. Pulse until finely chopped but still chunky, 4–5 times. Transfer to medium bowl, cover, and refrigerate until chilled, 2 hours or up to 6 hours.

2 Divide evenly among 4 bowls; sprinkle with avocado.

4 **SmartPoints value per serving** (1 cup soup and 2 tablespoons avocado): 125 Cal, 8 g Total Fat, 1 g Sat Fat, 656 mg Sod, 15 g Total Carb, 9 g Sugar, 4 g Fib, 3 g Prot.

Tip
If you have an abundance of melon on hand, try adding 1 cup of diced cantaloupe or watermelon to the gazpacho to lend a touch of sweetness. The SmartPoints value will remain the same.

Blender gazpacho
with avocado

Smoky corn soup

Serves 6

2	**teaspoons olive oil**
1	**small red onion, chopped**
1	**small red bell pepper, chopped**
1	**jalapeño pepper, seeded and chopped**
1	**garlic clove, minced**
1	**teaspoon salt**
½	**teaspoon smoked paprika**
½	**teaspoon ground cumin**
4	**small ears corn, kernels removed and cobs reserved**
4	**cups reduced-sodium vegetable broth**
¼	**cup light sour cream**
1	**tablespoon lime juice**
	Chopped fresh cilantro

1 Heat oil in Dutch oven over medium heat. Add onion, bell pepper, jalapeño, garlic, salt, paprika, and cumin, and cook, stirring often, until vegetables are softened, 5 minutes. Add corn kernels, corn cobs, and broth and bring to boil.

2 Reduce heat and simmer, covered, until vegetables are very tender, about 30 minutes. Remove and discard cobs. Let stand 5 minutes.

3 Transfer soup in batches to blender and puree. Return to Dutch oven and cook over low heat until hot, 2 minutes. Stir in sour cream and lime juice. Ladle evenly into 6 bowls and sprinkle with cilantro.

2 **SmartPoints value per serving** (generous 1 cup): 109 Cal, 4 g Total Fat, 1 g Sat Fat, 776 mg Sod, 18 g Total Carb, 5 g Sugar, 2 g Fib, 3 g Prot.

Tip
To cut corn kernels off the cobs, hold each ear at one end inside a large bowl and cut the kernels away with a sharp knife. Use the knife to scrape the cobs to extract more of their milky juices.

Asian peanut chicken salad

Serves 6

1   cup frozen shelled edamame
¼   cup smooth peanut butter
3   tablespoons hoisin sauce
3   tablespoons rice vinegar
2   tablespoons water
2   teaspoons reduced-sodium soy sauce
¾   teaspoon hot sauce
1   large scallion, sliced
1   teaspoon chopped peeled fresh ginger
¾   teaspoon salt
6   cups loosely packed thinly sliced Napa cabbage
2   cups shredded cooked skinless boneless chicken breast
2   large carrots, shredded
1   English (seedless) cucumber, halved lengthwise and thinly sliced
1   cup lightly packed whole fresh cilantro leaves

1 Bring small saucepan of water to boil over medium-high heat. Add edamame and cook 5 minutes. Drain, rinse under cold water, and pat dry. Transfer to large bowl.

2 Meanwhile, combine peanut butter, hoisin sauce, vinegar, water, soy sauce, hot sauce, scallion, ginger, and salt in blender and puree.

3 Add cabbage, chicken, carrots, cucumber, and cilantro to bowl with edamame. Add peanut-butter mixture and toss to combine. Serve immediately.

3 **SmartPoints value per serving** (1½ cups): 236 Cal, 9 g Total Fat, 2 g Sat Fat, 614 mg Sod, 18 g Total Carb, 9 g Sugar, 4 g Fib, 21 g Prot.

Tip
The peanut sauce for this salad is equally delicious served with grilled chicken or shrimp or as a dip for fresh veggies.

Peach, tomato,
and avocado salad

Peach, tomato, and avocado salad

Serves 4

¼ **cup loosely packed whole fresh flat-leaf parsley leaves**

¼ **cup loosely packed whole fresh cilantro leaves**

2 **tablespoons orange juice**

2 **teaspoons extra-virgin olive oil**

2 **teaspoons lime juice**

1 **teaspoon honey**

½ **teaspoon salt**

⅛ **teaspoon black pepper**

Pinch cayenne

3 **ripe peaches, pitted and cut into wedges**

2 **large tomatoes, cored and cut into wedges**

½ **small red onion, thinly sliced**

½ **ripe avocado, pitted, peeled, and diced**

1 To make vinaigrette, combine parsley, cilantro, orange juice, oil, lime juice, honey, salt, black pepper, and cayenne in mini–food processor and puree.

2 Arrange peaches, tomatoes, and onion on platter; sprinkle with avocado. Drizzle with vinaigrette and serve at once.

3 **SmartPoints value per serving** (¼ of salad): 136 Cal, 7 g Total Fat, 1 g Sat Fat, 300 mg Sod, 20 g Total Carb, 15 g Sugar, 5 g Fib, 3 g Prot.

Tip
To make this salad a summery main dish, top each serving with 3 ounces of grilled salmon for no additional SmartPoints.

Grilled Caesar salad with cherry tomatoes

Serves 4

1	**garlic clove**
3	**tablespoons grated Parmesan**
2	**tablespoons reduced-fat mayonnaise**
2	**anchovies, drained**
1	**tablespoon fresh lemon juice**
1	**tablespoon white balsamic vinegar**
1	**teaspoon Worcestershire sauce**
½	**teaspoon Dijon mustard**
½	**teaspoon agave nectar or honey**
⅛	**teaspoon black pepper**
4	**romaine lettuce hearts**
4	**(1-ounce) slices whole wheat Italian bread**
¼	**teaspoon salt**
2	**cups cherry tomatoes, halved**

1 Spray grill rack with nonstick spray. Preheat grill to medium-high or prepare medium-high fire.

2 Place garlic in mini–food processor and pulse until minced. Add 1 tablespoon of Parmesan, the mayonnaise, anchovies, lemon juice, vinegar, Worcestershire, mustard, agave nectar, and pepper; puree.

3 Cut each romaine heart lengthwise into halves or quarters if large, leaving cores intact. Pat dry with paper towels. Lightly spray romaine and bread with olive oil nonstick spray. Sprinkle romaine with salt.

4 Place lettuce on grill rack and grill, turning once, until lightly charred, but not limp, about 5 minutes. Place bread on grill rack and grill, turning once, until lightly charred, about 4 minutes. Cut bread into ½-inch cubes.

5 Arrange romaine evenly on 4 plates. Top with bread cubes and tomatoes. Drizzle evenly with dressing and sprinkle with remaining 2 tablespoons cheese. Serve at once.

4 **SmartPoints value per serving** (1 salad): 251 Cal, 7 g Total Fat, 1 g Sat Fat, 574 mg Sod, 39 g Total Carb, 13 g Sugar, 16 g Fib, 14 g Prot.

Tip
At farmers' markets or specialty food stores, look for a variety of lettuce called Little Gem for making these salads. It is a tender ruffle-leaved variety that is a cross between romaine and Bibb.

**Grilled Caesar salad
with cherry tomatoes**

**White bean pita burgers
with yogurt-tahini sauce**

White bean pita burgers with yogurt-tahini sauce

Serves 4

1	**(15-ounce) can cannellini (white kidney) beans, rinsed and drained**
¾	**cup whole wheat panko bread crumbs**
1	**carrot, finely shredded**
3	**tablespoons chopped fresh flat-leaf parsley**
1	**large egg**
½	**plus ⅛ teaspoon salt**
½	**teaspoon ground cumin**
¼	**teaspoon ground coriander**
⅛	**teaspoon cayenne**
3	**teaspoons olive oil**
¼	**cup plus 2 tablespoons plain fat-free Greek yogurt**
¼	**cup water**
1½	**tablespoons tahini**
1½	**tablespoons lemon juice**
1	**garlic clove, minced**
4	**(6-inch) whole wheat pita breads, halved**
8	**romaine or Bibb lettuce leaves**
8	**heirloom tomato slices, halved**

Lemon wedges

1 Place beans in large bowl. Using potato masher or fork, coarsely mash beans. Add panko, carrot, parsley, egg, ½ teaspoon of salt, ¼ teaspoon of cumin, coriander, and cayenne and stir to combine. Shape mixture into 8 small patties.

2 Heat 2 teaspoons of oil in large nonstick skillet over medium heat. Add patties and cook, turning once, until lightly browned, about 8 minutes.

3 Meanwhile, to make sauce, whisk together yogurt, water, tahini, lemon juice, garlic, remaining 1 teaspoon oil, remaining ⅛ teaspoon salt, and remaining ¼ teaspoon cumin in small bowl.

4 Line pita breads with lettuce leaves; fill with burgers and tomato slices. Drizzle with sauce. Serve with lemon wedges.

6 **SmartPoints value per serving** (2 filled pita halves and ¼ cup sauce): 352 Cal, 9 g Total Fat, 2 g Sat Fat, 942 mg Sod, 52 g Total Carb, 4 g Sugar, 9 g Fib, 17 g Prot.

Tip
Fresh shredded carrot lends a touch of sweetness and color to these burgers. They're fantastic topped with fresh summer tomato slices, but in winter, you can use sliced plum tomatoes instead.

Grilled Mediterranean chicken and vegetable wraps

Serves 4

¼   **cup white balsamic vinegar**

3   **garlic cloves, minced**

2   **teaspoons olive oil**

¼   **cup chopped fresh basil plus ½ cup whole basil leaves**

1   **pound thin-sliced skinless boneless chicken cutlets**

2   **assorted color bell peppers, quartered**

1   **Walla Walla or other sweet onion, halved and thickly sliced**

¾   **teaspoon salt**

¼   **teaspoon black pepper**

4   **(8-inch) multigrain or whole wheat sandwich wraps**

1   **large tomato, sliced**

½   **cup crumbled reduced-fat feta cheese**

1 Combine vinegar, garlic, oil, and ¼ cup of chopped basil in large bowl. Transfer half of vinegar mixture to medium bowl. Add chicken to medium bowl and toss to coat. Add bell peppers and onion to vinegar mixture in large bowl and toss to coat. Cover and refrigerate both 1 hour.

2 Spray grill rack and grill topper with nonstick spray. Preheat grill to medium or prepare medium fire.

3 Remove chicken and vegetables from marinade and discard marinade. Sprinkle chicken and vegetables with salt and black pepper. Place chicken on grill rack and vegetables on grill topper and grill, turning occasionally, until chicken is cooked through and vegetables are lightly browned and crisp-tender, 8 minutes for chicken and 10 minutes for vegetables. Thinly slice chicken and peppers.

4 Place one-fourth of chicken and vegetables on each wrap. Top evenly with remaining ½ cup whole basil leaves, tomato slices, and feta. Roll up and cut in half diagonally.

7 **SmartPoints value per serving** (1 wrap): 371 Cal, 12 g Total Fat, 4 g Sat Fat, 930 mg Sod, 32 g Total Carb, 10 g Sugar, 6 g Fib, 34 g Prot.

Tip

Bell peppers of every color are in abundance in late summer. Green bell peppers are immature and have a sharp, slightly bitter flavor. Red, orange, and yellow bell peppers are fully mature and therefore much sweeter.

Israeli couscous with tomato and olive sauté

Serves 8

1	**cup whole wheat Israeli couscous**
2	**teaspoons olive oil**
1	**shallot, chopped**
2	**garlic cloves, minced**
2	**cups grape or cherry tomatoes, halved**
¼	**teaspoon salt**
¼	**teaspoon black pepper**
¼	**cup pitted kalamata olives, halved**
⅓	**cup chopped fresh basil**
1	**teaspoon grated lemon zest**
1	**tablespoon lemon juice**

1 Cook couscous according to package directions.

2 Meanwhile, heat oil in medium nonstick skillet over medium heat. Add shallot and cook, stirring constantly, until softened, about 5 minutes. Add garlic and cook, stirring constantly, until fragrant, 30 seconds.

3 Add tomatoes, salt, and pepper. Cook, stirring occasionally, until tomatoes soften, about 6 minutes. Add olives and cook, stirring occasionally, just until heated through, about 1 minute.

4 Transfer couscous to serving bowl. Add tomato mixture, ¼ cup of basil, lemon zest, and lemon juice. Toss gently to combine. Sprinkle with remaining basil. Serve hot or at room temperature.

2 **SmartPoints value per serving** (about ⅔ cup): 91 Cal, 2 g Total Fat, 0 g Sat Fat, 106 mg Sod, 17 g Total Carb, 2 g Sugar, 2 g Fib, 3 g Prot.

Tip
Grape and cherry tomatoes are available year-round, but if you're at a farmers' market look for yellow, black, and zebra cherry tomatoes—interesting varieties you won't find at the supermarket.

Lemon-marinated grilled summer squash with dill

Serves 4

Grated zest and juice of 1 large lemon

1 **tablespoon olive oil**

1 **teaspoon white balsamic vinegar**

½ **teaspoon salt**

¼ **teaspoon black pepper**

2 **yellow summer squash, halved crosswise and cut lengthwise into thick slices**

2 **zucchini, halved crosswise and cut lengthwise into thick slices**

1 **tablespoon small fresh dill sprigs**

1 Spray grill rack with nonstick spray. Preheat grill to medium or prepare medium fire.

2 Stir together lemon zest and juice, oil, vinegar, salt, and pepper in large bowl. Add squash and zucchini and toss to coat. Let stand at room temperature about 15 minutes.

3 Remove vegetables from marinade; reserve marinade in bowl. Place vegetables on grill rack and grill, turning often, until lightly browned and crisp-tender, 8–10 minutes.

4 Return vegetables to bowl with marinade. Add dill and toss to coat. Serve warm, at room temperature, or chilled.

1 **SmartPoints value per serving** (about ¾ cup): 70 Cal, 4 g Total Fat, 1 g Sat Fat, 301 mg Sod, 8 g Total Carb, 6 g Sugar, 2 g Fib, 2 g Prot.

Tip

This colorful side dish is the perfect accompaniment to anything you put on the grill in the summer. Make a double batch and refrigerate to have for lunch later in the week.

Grilled Asian chicken with carrot-cucumber slaw

Serves 4

4	**(4-ounce) skinless boneless chicken breasts**
2	**tablespoons reduced-sodium soy sauce**
2	**tablespoons lime juice**
1	**garlic clove, minced**
2	**teaspoons chopped peeled fresh ginger**
2	**teaspoons honey**
2	**teaspoons canola oil**
1½	**teaspoons Asian (dark) sesame oil**
¾	**teaspoon salt**
3	**radishes, cut into matchstick strips**
1	**small carrot, cut into matchstick strips**
½	**English (seedless) cucumber, cut into matchstick strips**
2	**tablespoons minced fresh cilantro**
1	**tablespoon minced fresh mint**

1 Combine chicken, soy sauce, 1 tablespoon of lime juice, garlic, ginger, 1 teaspoon of honey, 1 teaspoon of canola oil, and 1 teaspoon of sesame oil in large zip-close plastic bag. Squeeze out air and seal bag; turn to coat chicken. Refrigerate 30 minutes.

2 Spray grill rack with nonstick spray. Preheat grill to medium or prepare medium fire.

3 Whisk together remaining 1 tablespoon lime juice, remaining 1 teaspoon honey, remaining 1 teaspoon canola oil, remaining ½ teaspoon sesame oil, and ¼ teaspoon of salt in small bowl and set aside. Combine radishes, carrot, cucumber, cilantro, and mint in large bowl and set aside.

4 Remove chicken from marinade and discard marinade. Sprinkle chicken with remaining ½ teaspoon of salt. Place on grill rack and grill, turning once, until cooked through, 6–8 minutes.

5 Add lime juice mixture to radish mixture and toss to coat. Serve chicken with salad.

2 **SmartPoints value per serving** (1 chicken cutlet and about ½ cup salad): 202 Cal, 7 g Total Fat, 1 g Sat Fat, 751 mg Sod, 7 g Total Carb, 4 g Sugar, 1 g Fib, 27 g Prot.

Tip
Continue the Asian theme of this meal by serving the chicken and slaw with rice noodles tossed with thinly sliced scallions (½ cup cooked rice noodles will increase the per-serving SmartPoints value by 3).

Grilled chicken with peach bbq sauce

Serves 6

3	teaspoons olive oil
1	small red onion, finely chopped
1	small garlic clove, minced
1	teaspoon chili powder
2	ripe peaches, pitted and sliced
1	cup strained tomatoes (see tip on page 98)
1	tablespoon tomato paste
¼	cup cider vinegar
1	teaspoon yellow mustard
¾	teaspoon salt
¼	teaspoon cayenne
6	(5-ounce) bone-in skinless chicken thighs, trimmed

1 Spray grill rack with nonstick spray. Preheat grill to medium or prepare medium fire.

2 Heat 1 teaspoon of oil in medium saucepan over medium heat. Add onion, garlic, and ½ teaspoon of chili powder and cook, stirring often, until onion begins to soften, 3 minutes. Add peaches, strained tomatoes, tomato paste, vinegar, mustard, ½ teaspoon of salt, and cayenne and bring to boil. Cook, stirring occasionally, until peaches are very tender, about 8 minutes. Let stand 5 minutes.

3 Transfer to blender and puree. Press puree through strainer and discard solids. (Sauce can be made up to 4 days ahead and stored in a covered container in refrigerator. Bring to room temperature before serving.)

4 Place chicken, remaining 2 teaspoons oil, remaining ½ teaspoon chili powder, and remaining ¼ teaspoon salt in medium bowl and turn chicken to coat. Place chicken on grill rack and grill, turning occasionally, until cooked through, 10–12 minutes, basting with ½ cup of sauce during last 5 minutes of grilling. Serve chicken with remaining sauce.

4 **SmartPoints value per serving** (1 chicken thigh and 2½ tablespoons sauce): 230 Cal, 8 g Total Fat, 2 g Sat Fat, 662 mg Sod, 9 g Total Carb, 7 g Sugar, 2 g Fib, 29 g Prot.

Tip
If you prefer a thicker sauce, place it in a saucepan and cook, uncovered, over medium heat until it reduces slightly, about 5 minutes.

Grilled chicken with peach bbq sauce and
Lemon-marinated grilled summer squash with dill, page 80

Chicken and eggplant stir-fry with snow peas

Serves 4

½   **cup reduced-sodium chicken broth**

¼   **cup reduced-sodium soy sauce**

3   **tablespoons mirin**

2   **teaspoons cornstarch**

2¼   **teaspoons Asian (dark) sesame oil**

1   **pound skinless boneless chicken breasts, cut into ½-inch cubes**

¼   **teaspoon salt**

½   **eggplant, cut into ½-inch cubes**

2   **garlic cloves, minced**

1   **tablespoon minced peeled fresh ginger**

6   **ounces snow peas, trimmed**

3   **scallions, thinly sliced**

1 To make sauce, whisk together broth, soy sauce, mirin, cornstarch, and ¼ teaspoon of oil in small bowl. Set aside.

2 Heat large deep skillet or wok over high heat until drop of water sizzles in pan. Add 1 teaspoon of oil and swirl to coat pan. Sprinkle chicken with salt and add to pan. Stir-fry until lightly browned, about 3 minutes. Transfer to plate.

3 Heat remaining 1 teaspoon of oil in pan. Add eggplant, garlic, and ginger and stir-fry until eggplant is softened, 5 minutes. Whisk sauce and add to skillet with chicken, snow peas, and scallions. Cook, stirring constantly, until sauce comes to boil and thickens and peas are crisp-tender, 1–2 minutes.

1   **SmartPoints value per serving** (1½ cups): 221 Cal, 6 g Total Fat, 1 g Sat Fat, 1,195 mg Sod, 9 g Total Carb, 4 g Sugar, 3 g Fib, 30 g Prot.

Tip

Bigger is not better when it comes to eggplant. Larger, more mature eggplants have bigger seeds so the cooked flesh often does not have a smooth texture. Look for firm eggplants with fresh green leaves at the stem end.

Steak with balsamic-molasses sauce and roasted green beans

Serves 4

1	**pound green beans, trimmed**
2	**teaspoons olive oil**
¾	**teaspoon salt**
½	**teaspoon salt-free steak grilling seasoning**
3	**tablespoons balsamic vinegar**
2	**tablespoons molasses**
¾	**teaspoon chopped fresh rosemary**
1	**(1-pound) lean boneless sirloin steak, trimmed**
¼	**teaspoon black pepper**
1	**shallot, finely chopped**
¼	**cup orange juice**

1 Preheat oven to 425°F.

2 Place green beans in large rimmed baking pan. Drizzle with oil and sprinkle with ½ teaspoon of salt and grilling seasoning. Spread in even layer and bake, stirring once, until lightly browned and crisp-tender, about 18 minutes.

3 Meanwhile, stir together vinegar, molasses, and rosemary in small bowl. Brush both sides of steak lightly with some of molasses mixture. Sprinkle steak with pepper and remaining ¼ teaspoon of salt.

4 Heat large heavy skillet over medium-high heat. Lightly spray steak with olive oil nonstick spray. Place steak in skillet and cook, turning once, until instant-read thermometer inserted into center of steak registers 145°F, 8–10 minutes. Transfer steak to cutting board and let stand 5 minutes.

5 Reduce heat to low. Add shallot and orange juice to skillet and cook, scraping up browned bits from bottom of pan, until shallot is softened, 2 minutes. Stir in remaining molasses mixture and bring to simmer. Remove from heat.

6 Cut steak across grain into 12 thin slices. Divide steak evenly among 4 plates and drizzle with sauce. Serve with green beans.

6 **SmartPoints value per serving** (3 slices steak, 1½ tablespoons sauce, and ¾ cup green beans): 253 Cal, 7 g Total Fat, 2 g Sat Fat, 516 mg Sod, 20 g Total Carb, 15 g Sugar, 3 g Fib, 28 g Prot.

Flank steak with cherry tomatoes and basil

Flank steak with cherry tomatoes and basil

Serves 4

1	**pound lean flank steak, trimmed**
¼	**cup plus 1 tablespoon balsamic vinegar**
¾	**teaspoon salt**
¼	**teaspoon black pepper**
3	**teaspoons olive oil**
2	**garlic cloves, minced**
3	**cups cherry tomatoes**
⅓	**cup chopped fresh basil**

1 Place steak in large shallow dish, drizzle with ¼ cup of vinegar, and turn to coat. Cover and refrigerate 30 minutes.

2 Remove steak from vinegar and pat dry with paper towels. Discard vinegar. Sprinkle steak with ½ teaspoon salt and the pepper.

3 Heat 2 teaspoons of oil in large heavy skillet over medium-high heat. Add steak and cook, turning occasionally, until instant-read thermometer inserted into center of steak registers 145°F, 8–10 minutes. Transfer to cutting board and let stand 5 minutes.

4 Meanwhile, heat remaining 1 teaspoon of oil in medium nonstick skillet over medium heat. Add garlic and cook, stirring constantly, until fragrant, 30 seconds. Add tomatoes and cook, stirring often, just until tomatoes begin to shrivel, about 4 minutes. Remove from heat and stir in remaining 1 tablespoon vinegar, basil, and remaining ¼ teaspoon salt. Cut steak thinly across grain into 12 slices. Serve steak with tomatoes.

5 **SmartPoints value per serving** (3 slices steak and about ⅔ cup tomatoes): 231 Cal, 10 g Total Fat, 3 g Sat Fat, 511 mg Sod, 8 g Total Carb, 6 g Sugar, 2 g Fib, 26 g Prot.

Tip
Don't use costly imported balsamic vinegar for this recipe. Inexpensive supermarket balsamic is all that's needed to infuse the steak with tangy flavor and give it a well-browned crust.

Bunless Asian beef burger wraps

Serves 4

1 **pound lean ground beef (7% fat or less)**

2 **small shallots, minced**

2 **tablespoons reduced-sodium soy sauce**

2 **teaspoons Asian fish sauce**

1 **teaspoon grated lime zest**

½ **teaspoon grated peeled fresh ginger**

2 **teaspoons canola oil**

½ **English (seedless) cucumber, thinly sliced**

1½ **tablespoons finely chopped fresh mint**

1 **tablespoon rice vinegar**

½ **teaspoon agave nectar**

¼ **teaspoon salt**

8 **large Bibb lettuce leaves**

1 Stir together beef, 1 shallot, soy sauce, 1 teaspoon of fish sauce, lime zest, and ginger in medium bowl. With damp hands, shape mixture into 8 (½-inch-thick) patties.

2 Heat oil in large nonstick skillet over medium heat. Add patties, and cook, turning once, until instant-read thermometer inserted into side of each patty registers 160°F, about 8 minutes.

3 Meanwhile, stir together remaining shallot, remaining 1 teaspoon fish sauce, cucumber, mint, vinegar, agave nectar, and salt in medium bowl.

4 Arrange 2 lettuce leaves onto each of 4 plates. Top with burgers. Top burgers evenly with cucumber mixture and roll up to enclose filling. Serve at once.

4 **SmartPoints value per serving** (2 garnished burgers): 199 Cal, 8 g Total Fat, 3 g Sat Fat, 713 mg Sod, 5 g Total Carb, 2 g Sugar, 1 g Fib, 26 g Prot.

Tip
English cucumbers are prized because of their undeveloped seeds and lack of bitterness, even when eaten unpeeled. Look for them at the supermarket wrapped in plastic wrap and at some farmers' markets, too.

**Bunless Asian
beef burger wraps**

Five-spice pork tenderloin with ginger plums

Five-spice pork tenderloin with ginger plums

Serves 4

1	**(1-pound) lean pork tenderloin, trimmed**
1¼	**teaspoons five-spice powder**
½	**teaspoon salt**
2	**teaspoons canola oil**
4	**ripe small plums, pitted and thinly sliced**
1	**tablespoon reduced-sodium soy sauce**
1	**tablespoon rice vinegar**
2	**teaspoons honey**
½	**teaspoon grated peeled fresh ginger**

1 Preheat oven to 400°F. Spray medium baking pan with nonstick spray.

2 Rub pork on all sides with five-spice powder and salt.

3 Heat oil in large skillet over medium-high heat. Add pork and cook, turning occasionally, until browned on all sides, about 8 minutes. Transfer pork to prepared baking pan. Do not wash skillet. Bake until instant-read thermometer inserted into center of pork registers 145°F, about 20 minutes. Let pork rest 5 minutes; then cut into 12 slices.

4 When pork is almost done, add plums, soy sauce, vinegar, honey, and ginger to same skillet and set over medium heat. Cook, stirring often, until plums are tender, about 4 minutes. Serve pork with plums.

3 **SmartPoints value per serving** (3 slices pork and about ⅓ cup plums): 186 Cal, 5 g Total Fat, 1 g Sat Fat, 480 mg Sod, 10 g Total Carb, 9 g Sugar, 1 g Fib, 25 g Prot.

Tip
Ripe plums should give a bit when gently pressed and feel slightly soft on the bottom. If yours are not ripe when you buy them, let them sit at room temperature for a day or two.

Flatbread prosciutto and salad pizza

Serves 4

1   **(8.8-ounce) package whole-grain naan flatbreads (2 naan per package)**

¼   **cup prepared sun-dried tomato pesto**

¾   **cup shredded reduced-fat Italian cheese blend**

¾   **teaspoon red pepper flakes**

2   **teaspoons olive oil**

2   **teaspoons lemon juice**

1   **teaspoon red-wine vinegar**

¼   **teaspoon salt**

1   **(5-ounce) container baby arugula (5 cups)**

4   **slices prosciutto, cut into thin strips**

2   **plum tomatoes, thinly sliced**

2   **tablespoons grated Parmesan cheese**

1 Preheat oven to 450°F.

2 Place flatbreads on large baking sheet. Spread tomato pesto on each, and sprinkle with cheese blend and red pepper flakes. Bake until bread is browned on bottom and cheese is melted, about 6 minutes.

3 Meanwhile, whisk together oil, lemon juice, vinegar, and salt in large bowl. When flatbreads are done, add arugula to bowl and toss to coat.

4 Top pizzas with prosciutto and tomatoes, then with arugula salad. Sprinkle with Parmesan. Cut each pizza into 2 pieces and serve at once.

11 **SmartPoints value per serving** (¼ of pizza): 378 Cal, 21 g Total Fat, 5 g Sat Fat, 1,046 mg Sod, 33 g Total Carb, 4 g Sugar, 5 g Fib, 18 g Prot.

Flatbread prosciutto
and salad pizza

Tandoori
roasted salmon
and vegetables

Tandoori roasted salmon and vegetables

Serves 4

1 teaspoon ground ginger
1 teaspoon garam masala
1 teaspoon ground coriander
¾ teaspoon salt
¼ teaspoon cayenne
¼ teaspoon sugar
2 pounds mixed zucchini and yellow squash, cut into ¼-inch slices
1 large shallot, thinly sliced
2 teaspoons olive oil
4 (5-ounce) skinless salmon fillets
3 tablespoons plain low-fat yogurt
Lemon wedges

1 Place one rack in upper third of oven. Preheat oven to 500°F. Spray large rimmed baking sheet with nonstick spray.

2 Stir together ginger, garam masala, coriander, salt, cayenne, and sugar in small bowl.

3 Place squash and shallot on prepared baking sheet. Drizzle with oil and 2 teaspoons of spice mixture and toss to coat. Spread in even layer around outer edge of pan. Place salmon in center of pan.

4 Add yogurt to remaining spice mixture in bowl; spoon over salmon. Bake in upper third of oven until fish is just opaque, 12–14 minutes. Serve with lemon wedges.

1 **SmartPoints value per serving** (1 fillet and 1 cup vegetables): 375 Cal, 22 g Total Fat, 5 g Sat Fat, 540 mg Sod, 13 g Total Carb, 8 g Sugar, 3 g Fib, 32 g Prot.

Tip
Plain fat-free yogurt mixed with a pinch of garam masala, a bit of grated lemon zest, and a few sprigs of chopped fresh cilantro makes a tangy ZeroPoint™ accompaniment for this dish.

Greek grilled fish and vegetable kebabs

Serves 4

2	tablespoons minced fresh thyme
1	tablespoon olive oil
2	garlic cloves, minced
½	teaspoon salt
¼	teaspoon black pepper
	Grated zest and juice of 2 lemons
1	pound swordfish or halibut, cut into 1-inch cubes
12	cherry tomatoes
1	small zucchini, cut into 8 pieces
1	red onion, cut into 8 wedges
1	red or orange bell pepper, cut into 1-inch pieces
	Lemon wedges

1 Whisk together thyme, oil, garlic, salt, pepper, and lemon zest and juice in medium bowl. Transfer half of thyme mixture to small bowl and set aside.

2 Add fish to thyme mixture remaining in medium bowl and toss to coat. Cover and refrigerate 30 minutes.

3 Spray grill rack with nonstick spray. Preheat grill to medium or prepare medium fire.

4 Remove fish from marinade; discard marinade. Thread fish, tomatoes, zucchini, onion, and bell pepper onto 4 (12-inch) metal skewers. Place skewers on grill rack and grill, turning occasionally, 10 minutes. Move kebabs to cooler part of grill and continue grilling until fish is just opaque in center and vegetables are crisp-tender, about 5 minutes. Transfer kebabs to serving platter and drizzle with remaining thyme mixture. Serve with lemon wedges.

1 **SmartPoints value per serving** (1 skewer): 233 Cal, 11 g Total Fat, 2 g Sat Fat, 390 mg Sod, 9 g Total Carb, 4 g Sugar, 2 g Fib, 24 g Prot.

Tip
If you are using disposable wooden skewers, soak them in water for 30 minutes before threading the fish and vegetables to keep them from burning on the grill.

**Greek grilled fish
and vegetable kebabs**

Skillet cod and summer vegetables

Serves 4

2	teaspoons olive oil
1	red onion, chopped
1	yellow bell pepper, diced
1	small zucchini, diced
½	eggplant, diced
1	garlic clove, minced
1	large tomato, diced
½	cup strained tomatoes
2	tablespoons tomato paste
1	teaspoon salt
¼	teaspoon black pepper
4	(5-ounce) pieces cod fillet
¼	cup chopped fresh basil

1 Heat oil in large nonstick skillet over medium heat. Add onion, bell pepper, zucchini, eggplant, and garlic, and cook, covered, stirring occasionally, until vegetables are softened, about 10 minutes. Add tomato, strained tomatoes, tomato paste, ½ teaspoon of salt, and ⅛ teaspoon of pepper and cook, stirring occasionally, until vegetables are tender, about 5 minutes.

2 Sprinkle fish with remaining ½ teaspoon of salt and remaining ⅛ teaspoon of pepper. Arrange fish in single layer on top of vegetables. Reduce heat to low, and simmer, covered, until fish is just opaque in center, about 10 minutes. Sprinkle with basil just before serving.

1 **SmartPoints value per serving** (1 fillet and 1½ cups vegetables): 181 Cal, 3 g Total Fat, 1 g Sat Fat, 1,202 mg Sod, 15 g Total Carb, 8 g Sugar, 4 g Fib, 24 g Prot.

Tip
Strained tomatoes have been peeled, seeded, and pureed. Look for them in jars or paper cartons in larger supermarkets or specialty stores. If you can't find them, use regular canned tomato puree.

Grilled vegetables and polenta

Serves 4

1	eggplant, cut into ½-inch slices
1	small zucchini, cut into ½-inch slices
1	small orange bell pepper, cut into 2-inch strips
1	small red bell pepper, cut into 2-inch strips
¼	cup white balsamic vinegar
1	tablespoon olive oil
3	garlic cloves, minced
¾	teaspoon salt
½	teaspoon black pepper
1½	cups chopped fresh basil
1	(16-ounce) tube fat-free polenta, cut into 12 (½-inch) slices
¼	cup freshly grated Parmigiano-Reggiano
2	tablespoons toasted pine nuts

1 Combine eggplant, zucchini, bell peppers, vinegar, oil, garlic, salt, and black pepper in large bowl and toss to coat.

2 Spray grill rack with nonstick spray. Preheat grill to medium or prepare medium fire.

3 Remove vegetables from marinade, reserving marinade. Place vegetables on grill rack and grill, turning occasionally, until lightly browned and crisp-tender, 6–8 minutes. Return vegetables to bowl with marinade. Add basil and toss to combine.

4 Meanwhile, lightly spray polenta slices with olive oil nonstick spray and place on grill rack. Grill, turning once, until lightly browned and heated through, about 6 minutes.

5 Divide polenta among 4 plates and top evenly with vegetables. Sprinkle with Parmigiano and pine nuts.

6 **SmartPoints value per serving** (3 slices polenta, 1¼ cups vegetables, 1 tablespoon cheese, and ½ tablespoon pine nuts): 227 Cal, 8 g Total Fat, 2 g Sat Fat, 856 mg Sod, 34 g Total Carb, 10 g Sugar, 6 g Fib, 7 g Prot.

Tip
To make this a heartier vegetarian main dish, add a 15-ounce can of small white beans, rinsed and drained, to the vegetables once they are grilled for no additional SmartPoints.

White bean and quinoa cakes

White bean and quinoa cakes

Serves 4

1   **cup water**
½   **cup quinoa, rinsed**
½   **cup canned small white beans,
      rinsed and drained**
3   **teaspoons olive oil**
1   **ear corn, kernels removed
      (½ cup)**
1   **large shallot, finely chopped**
½   **cup finely chopped orange or
      red bell pepper**
1   **garlic clove, minced**
¼   **cup whole wheat panko bread
      crumbs**
1   **large egg**
3   **tablespoons grated Parmesan**
½   **teaspoon salt**
⅛   **teaspoon black pepper**
2   **teaspoons minced fresh thyme**
Lemon wedges

1 Combine water and quinoa in small saucepan; bring to boil. Reduce heat and cover. Simmer until liquid is absorbed and quinoa is tender, about 10 minutes.

2 Meanwhile, place beans in large bowl and mash with fork or potato masher.

3 Drain quinoa in fine-mesh sieve and transfer to bowl with beans.

4 Heat 1 teaspoon of oil in large nonstick skillet over medium heat. Add corn, shallot, bell pepper, and garlic and cook, stirring often, until vegetables are tender, about 5 minutes. Add vegetable mixture, panko, egg, Parmesan, salt, black pepper, and thyme to quinoa mixture and stir to combine. Form mixture into 4 round cakes and chill 4 hours or overnight.

5 Add remaining 2 teaspoons oil to large nonstick skillet and set over medium heat. Place cakes in skillet and cook, carefully turning once, until lightly browned, about 8 minutes. Serve cakes with lemon wedges.

5 **SmartPoints value per serving** (1 cake): 241 Cal, 8 g Total Fat, 2 g Sat Fat, 531 mg Sod, 34 g Total Carb, 2 g Sugar, 5 g Fib, 11 g Prot.

Tip

These cakes are delicious on their own, or you can turn them into burgers by serving them in toasted whole wheat sandwich thins topped with lettuce and tomato (1 whole wheat sandwich thin will increase the per-serving SmartPoints value by 3).

Gemelli with tomatoes, limas, and arugula pesto

Serves 6

½ **pound whole wheat gemelli or penne**

1 **(10-ounce) package frozen baby lima beans, thawed**

1½ **cups loosely packed baby arugula**

1 **cup loosely packed fresh basil leaves**

2 **tablespoons olive oil**

2 **tablespoons lemon juice**

2 **tablespoons water**

2 **garlic cloves, peeled**

1 **teaspoon salt**

¼ **teaspoon black pepper**

2 **tablespoons grated pecorino Romano**

1½ **cups grape or cherry tomatoes, halved**

1 Cook gemelli according to package directions, adding lima beans during last 3 minutes of cooking time. Drain, reserving 1 cup cooking water. Transfer gemelli mixture to large bowl.

2 Meanwhile, to make pesto, puree arugula, basil, oil, lemon juice, water, garlic, salt, and pepper in food processor. Stir in pecorino.

3 Add pesto and tomatoes to gemelli mixture. Toss to coat, adding pasta cooking water ¼ cup at a time until mixture is moistened. Divide evenly among 4 shallow bowls.

5 **SmartPoints value per serving** (1 cup): 244 Cal, 6 g Total Fat, 1 g Sat Fat, 430 mg Sod, 40 g Total Carb, 3 g Sugar, 7 g Fib, 9 g Prot.

Blackberry cheesecake tarts

Makes 30

2 (1.9-ounce) packages frozen
   mini-phyllo tart shells

4 ounces reduced-fat cream
   cheese (Neufchâtel)

4 ounces fresh blackberries
   plus additional 30 blackberries
   for garnish

3 tablespoons plain low-fat
   Greek yogurt

2 tablespoons plus 1 teaspoon
   confectioners' sugar

½ teaspoon grated lemon zest

Pinch salt

1 Preheat oven to 350°F.

2 Place tart shells on large baking sheet and bake until crisp, 3–5 minutes. Transfer to wire rack and cool completely.

3 Meanwhile, combine cream cheese, 4 ounces of blackberries, yogurt, 2 tablespoons of confectioner's sugar, lemon zest, and salt in food processor and puree.

4 Spoon cream-cheese mixture evenly into phyllo shells. Top each tart with a blackberry (halve blackberries, if large) and sprinkle with remaining 1 teaspoon confectioners' sugar. Serve at once.

3 **SmartPoints value per serving** (3 tarts): 86 Cal, 3 g Total Fat, 1 g Sat Fat, 115 mg Sod, 12 g Total Carb, 4 g Sugar, 1 g Fib, 3 g Prot.

Blueberry-peach cornmeal cupcakes

Makes 12

1   cup all-purpose flour
1   cup cornmeal
2   teaspoons baking powder
½   teaspoon baking soda
½   teaspoon salt
1¼ cups low-fat buttermilk
½   cup granulated sugar
2   large eggs
2   tablespoons olive oil
2   teaspoons vanilla extract
1   teaspoon grated lemon zest
1   ripe peach, peeled, pitted, and diced (about 1 cup)
1   cup fresh or frozen blueberries
1   tablespoon confectioners' sugar

1 Preheat oven to 350°F. Spray 12-cup muffin pan with cooking spray.

2 Whisk together flour, cornmeal, baking powder, baking soda, and salt in medium bowl. Whisk together buttermilk, granulated sugar, eggs, oil, vanilla, and lemon zest in large bowl. Add flour mixture to buttermilk mixture and stir just until flour mixture is moistened. Gently stir in peach and blueberries.

3 Fill muffin cups evenly with batter. Bake until toothpick inserted into centers comes out clean, 18–20 minutes. Let cool in pan on wire rack 5 minutes. Remove cupcakes from pan and cool completely on rack. Just before serving, dust with confectioners' sugar.

6   **SmartPoints value per serving** (1 cupcake): 177 Cal, 4 g Total Fat, 1 g Sat Fat, 270 mg Sod, 31 g Total Carb, 13 g Sugar, 1 g Fib, 4 g Prot.

Tip
Perfect for dessert or breakfast on-the-go, these simple cupcakes get most of their sweetness from the peaches' natural sugars. You can substitute nectarines, if you prefer.

Blueberry-peach cornmeal cupcakes

Plum and blackberry crisp with pistachio crumble

Plum and blackberry crisp with pistachio crumble

Serves 8

4   large ripe plums, pitted and thinly sliced (about 3 cups)

3   cups fresh blackberries

2   tablespoons all-purpose flour

2   teaspoons grated lemon zest

¼   teaspoon ground cardamom

½   cup old-fashioned oats

¼   cup packed light brown sugar

2   tablespoons unsalted butter

¼   teaspoon salt

¼   cup finely chopped pistachios

1 Preheat oven to 350°F. Spray 8-inch square baking dish with nonstick spray.

2 Combine plums, blackberries, flour, lemon zest, and cardamom in large bowl and toss to coat evenly. Pour fruit mixture into prepared baking dish.

3 Combine oats, brown sugar, butter, and salt in medium bowl. Using your fingers, blend butter evenly into oat mixture. Stir in pistachios. Sprinkle evenly over fruit mixture.

4 Bake until topping is golden brown and fruit is soft and bubbling, 30–35 minutes. Transfer to wire rack. Let cool at least 15 minutes before serving. Serve hot or warm.

4 **SmartPoints value per serving** (about ¾ cup): 131 Cal, 5 g Total Fat, 2 g Sat Fat, 75 mg Sod, 19 g Total Carb, 11 g Sugar, 4 g Fib, 3 g Prot.

Tip
Let your market and your pantry guide you when making this adaptable recipe. Instead of plums try ripe peaches, and instead of blackberries, use blueberries or raspberries. Don't care for cardamom? Substitute the same amount of cinnamon.

Melon with ginger-mint syrup

Serves 4

⅓	**cup water**
2	**tablespoons agave nectar**
1	**tablespoon fresh lime juice**
½	**teaspoon grated peeled fresh ginger**
¼	**teaspoon salt**
	Grated zest of ½ lime
4	**cups any combination of cantaloupe, watermelon, and honeydew balls**
1	**tablespoon finely chopped fresh mint**
1	**tablespoon thinly sliced crystallized ginger**

1 Combine water, agave nectar, lime juice, fresh ginger, and ⅛ teaspoon of salt in small saucepan; bring to boil over medium-high heat. Cook, stirring occasionally, until mixture is reduced to scant ¼ cup, about 6 minutes. Transfer to medium bowl and stir in lime zest. Let stand to cool.

2 Add melon, remaining ⅛ teaspoon salt, mint, and crystallized ginger to bowl and toss gently to combine. Serve at once.

② **SmartPoints value per serving** (1 cup fruit with 1 tablespoon syrup): 90 Cal, 0 g Total Fat, 0 g Sat Fat, 167 mg Sod, 23 g Total Carb, 20 g Sugar, 2 g Fib, 1 g Prot.

Tip
This refreshing melon dessert makes a satisfying summer breakfast, too. Enjoy it with ½ cup plain fat-free Greek yogurt for no additional SmartPoints.

**Melon with
ginger-mint syrup**

Plum and ricotta trifle with almonds

Serves 16

1	**large orange**
4	**large ripe plums or 3 ripe nectarines, pitted and thinly sliced (3 cups)**
1	**teaspoon almond extract**
½	**teaspoon salt**
1	**(32-ounce) container fat-free ricotta cheese**
¼	**cup honey**
¼	**teaspoon cinnamon**
⅛	**teaspoon ground nutmeg**
24	**Italian ladyfinger cookies**
9	**tablespoons crème de cassis liqueur**
6	**tablespoons slivered almonds, toasted**

1 Grate 1 teaspoon zest from orange and squeeze 2 tablespoons juice.

2 Stir together plums, orange juice, almond extract, and ¼ teaspoon of salt in medium bowl.

3 Puree ricotta, honey, cinnamon, nutmeg, and remaining ¼ teaspoon salt in food processor. Add orange zest and pulse until blended.

4 Arrange 8 cookies in bottom of trifle dish or large glass bowl; drizzle with 3 tablespoons of crème de cassis. Top with 1 cup of plum mixture. Top plum mixture with 1 cup of ricotta mixture and sprinkle with 2 tablespoons of almonds. Repeat layering two more times.

5 Cover and refrigerate 4 hours or overnight.

6  **SmartPoints value per serving** (¹⁄₁₆ of trifle): 179 Cal, 3 g Total Fat, 1 g Sat Fat, 208 mg Sod, 25 g Total Carb, 19 g Sugar, 1 g Fib, 11 g Prot.

Tip
It's not likely that you'll find perfectly ripe plums in the supermarket or at a farmers' market. Buy plums a couple of days before you make the trifle and leave at room temperature to achieve just the right ripeness.

Almond-cherry oat bars

Makes 16

1	**cup white whole wheat flour**
⅔	**cup old-fashioned oats**
½	**cup chopped almonds, toasted**
1	**teaspoon cinnamon**
½	**teaspoon baking powder**
¼	**teaspoon baking soda**
¼	**teaspoon salt**
½	**cup packed dark brown sugar**
¼	**cup olive oil**
2	**large egg whites**
2	**tablespoons creamy almond butter**
½	**teaspoon vanilla extract**
¾	**cup fresh sweet cherries, pitted and halved, or unsweetened frozen pitted cherries, halved**

1 Preheat oven to 350°F. Line 8-inch square baking pan with parchment paper, allowing paper to extend over rim of pan by 2 inches.

2 Stir together flour, oats, almonds, cinnamon, baking powder, baking soda, and salt in large bowl. Stir together brown sugar, oil, egg whites, almond butter, and vanilla in medium bowl. Add brown sugar mixture and cherries to flour mixture and stir to combine. Transfer mixture to prepared pan and pat evenly into pan with damp hands.

3 Bake until golden brown and toothpick inserted into center comes out clean, about 25 minutes. Let cool completely in pan on wire rack. Lift from pan using parchment paper as handles. Cut lengthwise into 4 strips; then cut each strip across into 4 squares.

5 **SmartPoints value per serving** (1 bar): 132 Cal, 6 g Total Fat, 1 g Sat Fat, 80 mg Sod, 16 g Total Carb, 9 g Sugar, 1 g Fib, 3 g Prot.

Tip
If you prefer, make these bars with fresh blueberries or with chopped peeled fresh peaches instead of the cherries.

Sweet
potatoes

Butternut
squash

Kale

Figs

Golden
acorn squash

Broccoflower

Chapter 3

Fall

Enjoy the bounty of comforting dishes when chilly weather returns.

Spinach

Apples

Cipollini onions

In this chapter

What's in season

- Apples
- Asian pears
- Beets
- Broccoli
- Broccoli rabe
- Butternut squash
- Carrots
- Cauliflower
- Celery root
- Cranberries
- Figs
- Grapes
- Hubbard squash
- Kabocha squash
- Kale
- Leeks
- Mushrooms
- Onions
- Pears
- Pomegranates
- Potatoes
- Savoy cabbage
- Spinach
- Sugar pumpkins
- Sweet potatoes
- Swiss chard
- Turnips

Sweet potato muffins with pecan streusel

Makes 12

Streusel

2	tablespoons packed brown sugar
2	tablespoons quick-cooking oats
2	tablespoons chopped pecans
1½	teaspoons cinnamon
1½	teaspoons canola oil

Muffins

1	cup all-purpose flour
½	cup whole wheat flour
¼	cup granulated sugar
¼	cup packed brown sugar
1½	teaspoons baking powder
¾	teaspoon ground ginger
½	teaspoon baking soda
½	teaspoon cinnamon
¼	teaspoon salt
1	cup mashed sweet potato
⅔	cup low-fat buttermilk
2	tablespoons canola oil
1	large egg

1 Preheat oven to 375°F. Line 12-cup muffin pan with paper liners.

2 To make streusel, stir together brown sugar, oats, pecans, and cinnamon in small bowl until blended. Stir in oil.

3 To make muffins, whisk together all-purpose flour, whole wheat flour, granulated sugar, brown sugar, baking powder, ginger, baking soda, cinnamon, and salt in large bowl. Whisk together sweet potato, buttermilk, oil, and egg in medium bowl. Add sweet potato mixture to flour mixture and stir until moistened (batter will be thick).

4 Spoon batter into prepared muffin cups and sprinkle evenly with streusel. Bake until toothpick inserted into center of muffins comes out clean, about 20 minutes. Cool in pan on wire rack 10 minutes. Remove muffins from pan and cool completely on rack.

6 **SmartPoints value per serving** (1 muffin): 167 Cal, 5 g Total Fat, 1 g Sat Fat, 261 mg Sod, 29 g Total Carb, 13 g Sugar, 2 g Fib, 3 g Prot.

Tip
To get 1 cup mashed sweet potato, bake 1 large sweet potato at 400°F for 1 hour or until tender. Cut lengthwise in half and open up to let cool before scooping flesh out and mashing.

Sausage, kale, and Cheddar frittata

Serves 4

1	(½-pound) bunch kale, stems discarded and leaves coarsely chopped
1	medium red potato (3 ounces), scrubbed
5	large egg whites
4	large eggs
¾	teaspoon salt
¼	teaspoon black pepper
½	cup shredded reduced-fat sharp Cheddar cheese
2	teaspoons olive oil
6	fully cooked turkey breakfast sausages, coarsely chopped
1	large red onion, chopped

1 Preheat oven to 375°F.

2 Bring large saucepan of water to boil over high heat. Add kale and cook just until tender, 3–5 minutes. Drain and let cool. Squeeze excess water from kale.

3 Meanwhile, pierce potato in several places with knife and place in medium microwavable bowl. Cover with wax paper and microwave on High until potato is tender, about 5 minutes. Transfer potato to plate to cool slightly. Dice potato.

4 Whisk together egg whites, eggs, salt, and pepper in medium bowl. Stir in all but 2 tablespoons of Cheddar.

5 Heat 1 teaspoon of oil in 10-inch ovenproof nonstick skillet over medium heat. Add sausages and cook, stirring occasionally, until sausages are lightly browned. Transfer to plate.

6 Add remaining 1 teaspoon oil to skillet. Add onion and cook, stirring occasionally until onion is softened and browned, about 10 minutes.

7 Add potato, kale, and sausage to skillet in even layer. Pour in egg mixture and spread evenly over vegetable mixture. Reduce heat to medium-low and cook until edges set, about 4 minutes. Transfer skillet to oven and bake just until set in center, 15 minutes.

8 Sprinkle frittata with remaining 2 tablespoons cheese. Bake until cheese melts, about 1 minute longer. Cut into 4 wedges.

4 **SmartPoints value per serving** (1 wedge): 259 Cal, 14 g Total Fat, 4 g Sat Fat, 1,025 mg Sod, 12 g Total Carb, 3 g Sugar, 3 g Fib, 23 g Prot.

Sausage, kale, and
Cheddar frittata

Gingerbread
pancakes
with pears

Gingerbread pancakes with pears

Serves 8

1   teaspoon unsalted butter

4   small firm-ripe pears, peeled, cored, and sliced

1¾   cups reduced-fat buttermilk baking mix

1   teaspoon cinnamon

½   teaspoon ground ginger

¾   cup fat-free milk

1   large egg

1   tablespoon light molasses

2   teaspoons canola oil

4   teaspoons pure maple syrup

1 Melt butter in large nonstick skillet over medium heat. Add pears and cook, stirring occasionally, until pears are tender, about 5 minutes. Remove from heat and set aside.

2 Meanwhile, whisk together baking mix, cinnamon, and ginger in medium bowl. Whisk together milk, egg, and molasses in small bowl until smooth (molasses may clump when added to cold ingredients; let stand 2–3 minutes to soften and whisk until smooth). Add milk mixture to baking-mix mixture and stir just until blended.

3 Heat 1 teaspoon of oil on nonstick griddle or in large nonstick skillet over medium heat. Pour batter by ¼-cup measures onto griddle. Cook just until bubbles begin to appear at edges of pancakes, about 3 minutes. Flip and cook until browned, about 2 minutes. Repeat with remaining oil and batter to make a total of 8 pancakes. Top pancakes with pears and drizzle with maple syrup.

6   **SmartPoints value per serving** (1 pancake and about ¼ cup pears): 214 Cal, 4 g Total Fat, 1 g Sat Fat, 401 mg Sod, 42 g Total Carb, 15 g Sugar, 3 g Fib, 4 g Prot.

Tip
If you live in a region where maple syrup is locally produced, look for it at farmers' markets and outdoor festivals and stock up on this artisanal treat. If you live where sugar maples don't grow, you can find it in most supermarkets.

Cranberry-pear breakfast porridge

Serves 4

3   cups water
½   cup quick-cooking barley
½   cup bulgur
½   cup old-fashioned oats
⅓   cup dried cranberries
¼   teaspoon salt
½   cup fat-free milk
2   tablespoons pure maple syrup
1   large firm-ripe pear, peeled, cored, and diced
4   teaspoons toasted sunflower seeds

1 Bring water to boil in large saucepan. Stir in barley, bulgur, oats, cranberries, and salt. Reduce heat and simmer, stirring occasionally, until most of water is absorbed and grains are tender but still chewy, about 13 minutes.

2 Divide cereal evenly among 4 bowls. Drizzle evenly with milk and maple syrup; sprinkle with pear and sunflower seeds. Serve at once.

9 **SmartPoints value per serving** (about ⅔ cup porridge, ½ tablespoon syrup, and 1 teaspoon sunflower seeds): 249 Cal, 3 g Total Fat, 0 g Sat Fat, 170 mg Sod, 53 g Total Carb, 23 g Sugar, 7 g Fib, 6 g Prot.

Tip
This cereal reheats well in the microwave, so it's a good choice to have on hand for mornings when time is limited. Add a few tablespoons water to each serving when reheating.

Fall fruit and yogurt breakfast bowls

Serves 2

1½ **cups plain fat-free Greek yogurt**

1½ **teaspoons honey**

1   **cup grapes, halved**

4   **fresh figs, quartered**

¼   **cup pomegranate arils
     (to remove arils, see tip on
     page 175)**

1 Whisk together yogurt and honey in medium bowl.

2 Divide yogurt mixture evenly between 2 bowls. Top with grapes and figs; sprinkle with pomegranate arils. Serve at once.

1 **SmartPoints value per serving** (¾ cup ricotta mixture, ¾ cup fruit, and 2 tablespoons pomegranate seeds): 260 Cal, 1 g Total Fat, 0 g Sat Fat, 66 mg Sod, 47 g Total Carb, 41 g Sugar, 4 g Fib, 19 g Prot.

Irish oatmeal with brown sugar–cinnamon roasted apples

Serves 4

2	**Honeycrisp or Rome apples, cored and cut into 1-inch chunks**
1	**tablespoon packed brown sugar**
½	**teaspoon ground cinnamon**
3	**cups water**
⅛	**teaspoon salt**
1	**cup steel-cut oats**
2	**tablespoons golden raisins**
2	**tablespoons chopped toasted walnuts**

1 Preheat oven to 375°F. Line rimmed baking sheet with parchment paper.

2 Combine apples, brown sugar, and cinnamon in medium bowl and toss to coat. Place apples on prepared baking sheet and spread in single layer. Bake, stirring once, until apples are tender about 30 minutes.

3 Meanwhile, bring water and salt to boil in large saucepan. Stir in oats and raisins. Reduce heat and simmer, stirring often, until liquid is absorbed and oatmeal is tender, but still chewy, about 30 minutes.

4 Divide oatmeal among 4 bowls and top with apples and walnuts.

7 **SmartPoints value per serving** (⅔ cup oatmeal, about ½ cup apples, and ½ tablespoon walnuts): 249 Cal, 5 g Total Fat, 0 g Sat Fat, 81 mg Sod, 47 g Total Carb, 17 g Sugar, 7 g Fib, 6 g Prot.

Irish oatmeal with
brown sugar–cinnamon
roasted apples

Maple muesli with apples and pecans

Serves 4

1	**cup rolled oats**
2	**cups plain low-fat yogurt**
2	**tablespoons golden raisins**
1	**tablespoon maple syrup**
½	**teaspoon cinnamon**
2	**small apples or pears or a combination, cored and chopped**
2	**tablespoons toasted chopped pecans**

1 Stir together oats, yogurt, raisins, maple syrup, and cinnamon in small bowl. Cover and refrigerate overnight.

2 Divide oat mixture evenly among 4 bowls. Top evenly with apples and pecans.

8 **SmartPoints value per serving** (1 bowl): 244 Cal, 6 g Total Fat, 2 g Sat Fat, 89 mg Sod, 40 g Total Carb, 23 g Sugar, 5 g Fib, 10 g Prot.

Lentil and chorizo soup with kale

Serves 4

1	onion, chopped
2	fully cooked chicken chorizo sausages (6 ounces), diced
4	garlic cloves, minced
1	(½-pound) bunch kale, stems discarded and leaves coarsely chopped
3	cups reduced-sodium chicken broth
3	cups water
1	cup brown lentils, picked over and rinsed
¾	teaspoon salt
2	large plum tomatoes, diced
¼	teaspoon smoked paprika

1 Spray Dutch oven with nonstick spray and set over medium heat. Add onion and chorizo and cook, stirring occasionally, until onion is golden, about 10 minutes. Add garlic and cook, stirring constantly, until fragrant, 30 seconds. Add kale and cook, stirring often, until kale is wilted, about 3 minutes. Stir in broth, water, and lentils. Cover and bring to boil; reduce heat and simmer, covered, until lentils are tender, about 45 minutes. Stir in salt.

2 Meanwhile, spray medium skillet with nonstick spray and set over medium heat. Add tomatoes and paprika and cook, stirring, until tomatoes soften, about 2 minutes. Serve soup topped with tomato mixture.

3 **SmartPoints value per serving** (2 cups soup and ¼ cup tomato mixture): 296 Cal, 5 g Total Fat, 1 g Sat Fat, 1,147 mg Sod, 40 g Total Carb, 5 g Sugar, 9 g Fib, 23 g Prot.

**Smoky sweet potato
and black bean soup**

Smoky sweet potato and black bean soup

Serves 8

2   teaspoons olive oil

1   onion, chopped

2   garlic cloves, minced

2   teaspoons ground cumin

2   large sweet potatoes
    (1¾ pounds), peeled and cut
    into ½-inch pieces (6 cups)

2   cups water

¾   teaspoon salt

2   cups reduced-fat (2%) milk

1½ cups frozen corn kernels

1   (15½-ounce) can black beans,
    rinsed and drained

2   teaspoons minced chipotles
    en adobo

Fresh cilantro

Thinly sliced scallions

Lime wedges

1 Heat oil in Dutch oven over medium-high heat. Add onion and cook, stirring often, until softened, 5 minutes. Add garlic and cumin and cook, stirring constantly, until fragrant, about 1 minute.

2 Add sweet potatoes, water, and salt and bring to boil. Reduce heat and simmer, covered, until vegetables are very tender, about 10 minutes.

3 Transfer 2 cups of sweet-potato mixture to food processor and puree. Return puree to Dutch oven. Add milk, corn, black beans, and chipotles. Reduce heat to low and cook covered, stirring occasionally, just until heated through (do not boil), about 5 minutes. Ladle evenly into 6 bowls; sprinkle with cilantro and scallions. Serve with lime wedges.

5 **SmartPoints value per serving** (generous 1 cup): 210 Cal, 3 g Total Fat, 1 g Sat Fat, 526 mg Sod, 40 g Total Carb, 9 g Sugar, 8 g Fib, 8 g Prot.

Pumpkin-ginger bisque

Serves 6

1   teaspoon olive oil
1   onion, chopped
2   garlic cloves, minced
1   tablespoon grated peeled fresh ginger
1   (32-ounce) container reduced-sodium vegetable broth
3   pounds sugar pumpkin or butternut squash, peeled, seeded, and cut into 1-inch chunks (6 cups)
1   large Granny Smith apple, peeled, cored, and cut into ½-inch pieces
¾   teaspoon salt
¼   teaspoon black pepper
¼   cup light sour cream
3   tablespoons toasted pumpkin seeds

1 Heat oil in large Dutch oven over medium-high heat. Add onion and cook, covered, stirring occasionally, until golden, 5 minutes. Add garlic and ginger and cook, stirring constantly, until fragrant, 30 seconds.

2 Add broth, pumpkin, apple, salt, and pepper and bring to boil. Reduce heat and simmer, partially covered, until pumpkin is very tender, about 30 minutes.

3 Remove saucepan from heat and let soup cool 5 minutes. Puree soup in blender in batches.

4 Return soup to Dutch oven. Cook over medium heat, stirring occasionally, until heated through, about 2 minutes. Remove from heat and whisk in sour cream. Serve sprinkled with pumpkin seeds.

2 **SmartPoints value per serving** (1 cup soup and ½ tablespoon pumpkin seeds): 134 Cal, 4 g Total Fat, 1 g Sat Fat, 437 mg Sod, 25 g Total Carb, 12 g Sugar, 3 g Fib, 4 g Prot.

Tip
Sugar pumpkins, sometimes called pie pumpkins, are smaller than the jack-o-lantern carving variety and better for cooking. The flesh is smoother and has a more pronounced pumpkin flavor.

Pear and fig salad with blue cheese

Serves 4

1	tablespoon finely chopped
	shallot
1	tablespoon rice vinegar
½	teaspoon grated orange zest
1	tablespoon orange juice
1½	teaspoons olive oil
½	teaspoon Dijon mustard
¼	teaspoon salt
⅛	teaspoon black pepper
4	cups torn escarole
2	cups loosely packed baby
	salad greens
1	Asian pear, cored
	and sliced
8	fresh figs, stemmed and
	quartered
¼	cup crumbled reduced-fat
	blue cheese
2	tablespoons toasted hazelnuts,
	coarsely chopped

1 To make dressing, whisk together shallot, vinegar, orange zest and juice, oil, mustard, salt, and pepper in large bowl.

2 Add escarole, salad greens, and pear and toss to coat. Add figs, blue cheese, and hazelnuts and toss gently to combine.

2 **SmartPoints value per serving** (about 2 cups): 166 Cal, 6 g Total Fat, 1 g Sat Fat, 267 mg Sod, 27 g Total Carb, 19 g Sugar, 7 g Fib, 5 g Prot.

Tip
Asian pears are sometimes called apple pears because of their crisp texture. Use a regular pear or an apple in this salad if you prefer.

Roasted beet and carrot salad

Serves 4

1	**pound baby carrots, halved lengthwise**
2	**teaspoons olive oil**
1	**pound beets, peeled and cut into 2 x ½-inch pieces**
½	**teaspoon grated lime zest**
2	**tablespoons lime juice**
1	**tablespoon red-wine vinegar**
1	**teaspoon honey**
½	**teaspoon salt**
¼	**cup chopped fresh cilantro**
2	**scallions, thinly sliced**
4	**cups loosely packed baby arugula or baby salad greens**
¼	**cup crumbled reduced-fat feta cheese**

1 Preheat oven to 375°F. Spray large rimmed baking sheet with nonstick spray.

2 Toss carrots with ¼ teaspoon of oil in medium bowl. Spread carrots on half of prepared baking sheet. Toss beets in same bowl with ¼ teaspoon of oil. Spread beets on other half of baking sheet. Bake, stirring once and keeping vegetables separate, until vegetables are tender, about 30 minutes.

3 Meanwhile, to make dressing, whisk together remaining 1½ teaspoons oil, lime zest and juice, vinegar, honey, and salt in small bowl.

4 While vegetables are warm, toss beets with half of dressing in medium bowl. Toss carrots with remaining dressing in another medium bowl. Let stand until cool, stirring occasionally, about 15 minutes.

5 Combine beets, carrots, cilantro, and scallions in large bowl. (The salad can be made a day ahead up to this point; cover and refrigerate until ready to serve.) Divide salad greens among 4 plates. Top evenly with beet and carrot salad. Sprinkle with feta.

2 **SmartPoints value per serving** (1 cup beet and carrot salad, 1 cup greens, and 1 tablespoon cheese): 153 Cal, 5 g Total Fat, 1 g Sat Fat, 561 mg Sod, 27 g Total Carb, 15 g Sugar, 8 g Fib, 6 g Prot.

Tip
Look for beets with the tops still attached for a double treat. Remove the tough stems from the greens, chop the leaves, and steam or sauté them with a little garlic for a flavorful and healthy side dish.

Roasted beet
and carrot salad

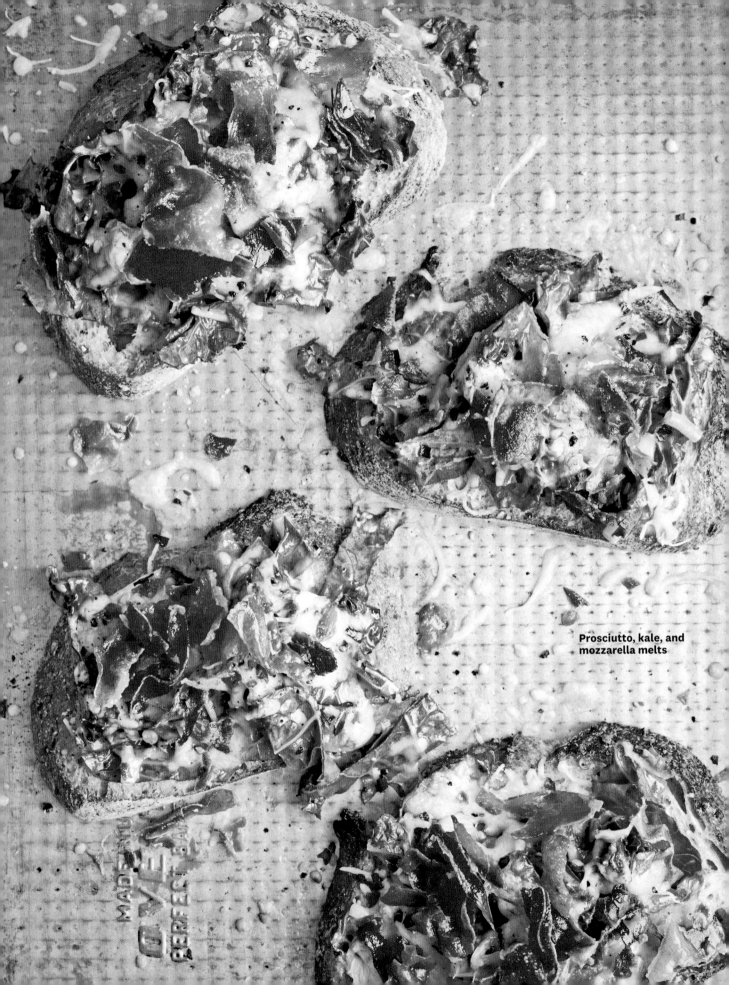

Prosciutto, kale, and mozzarella melts

Prosciutto, kale, and mozzarella melts

Serves 6

2   ounces prosciutto

3   garlic cloves, minced

⅛   teaspoon red pepper flakes

1   (½-pound) bunch kale, stems
     removed and leaves thinly sliced

3   tablespoons water

⅛   teaspoon salt

6   (1-ounce) slices whole-grain
     bread, toasted

2   tablespoons grated Parmesan

¾   cup shredded part-skim
     mozzarella

1 Preheat oven to 400°F. Spray large rimmed baking sheet with nonstick spray.

2 Arrange prosciutto on prepared baking sheet in single layer. Bake until crisp, 5–6 minutes. Transfer prosciutto to plate. Maintain oven temperature. Do not wash baking sheet.

3 Meanwhile, spray large skillet with nonstick spray and set over medium heat. Add garlic and pepper flakes. Cook, stirring constantly, until fragrant, 30 seconds. Add half of kale and cook, stirring often, until wilted, about 1 minute. Add remaining kale and the water. Cook, stirring often, until kale is crisp-tender and water evaporates, about 5 minutes. Stir in salt.

4 Arrange bread on same baking sheet and sprinkle with Parmesan. Top evenly with kale; then sprinkle with mozzarella. Bake until cheese melts, about 5 minutes. Crumble prosciutto and sprinkle over sandwiches.

5 **SmartPoints value per serving** (1 open-face sandwich): 170 Cal, 7 g Total Fat, 3 g Sat Fat, 630 mg Sod, 15 g Total Carb, 2 g Sugar, 4 g Fib, 13 g Prot.

Tip
There are two types of kale: curly kale and flat-leaf kale (also called Tuscan, dinosaur, or lacinato kale). Generally they are interchangeable in recipes, but the flat-leaf kale is a bit more tender and takes a few minutes less time to cook.

Chicken sausage and mushroom hoagies

Serves 4

1 teaspoon olive oil

3 fully cooked hot Italian chicken sausages (8 ounces), sliced

1 red onion, halved and thinly sliced

½ pound cremini mushrooms, sliced

2 garlic cloves, minced

¼ teaspoon salt

4 (6-inch) whole wheat hoagie rolls (3 ounces each), split

¼ cup hoisin sauce

½ cup shredded part-skim mozzarella

¼ cup chopped fresh cilantro

1 scallion, thinly sliced

1 Heat oil in large skillet over medium-high heat. Add sausage and cook, stirring occasionally, until lightly browned, 5–6 minutes. With slotted spoon, transfer sausage to plate. Add onion to skillet and cook, stirring occasionally, until softened, about 7 minutes. Stir in mushrooms, garlic, and salt. Cook, stirring often, until mushrooms are tender, about 8 minutes.

2 Preheat broiler. Pull out some of soft centers from rolls. Place cut sides up on broiler pan. Broil 5 inches from heat until toasted, about 1 minute.

3 Spread hoisin sauce on cut sides of rolls. Top bottom halves of rolls with mushroom mixture. Arrange sausage on top halves of rolls. Sprinkle mozzarella evenly over rolls. Broil 5 inches from heat until cheese melts, about 1 minute. Sprinkle rolls with cilantro and scallions and then close with roll tops.

12 **SmartPoints value per serving** (1 sandwich): 406 Cal, 12 g Total Fat, 3 g Sat Fat, 1,160 mg Sod, 56 g Total Carb, 15 g Sugar, 8 g Fib, 22 g Prot.

Tip
Cremini mushrooms are baby portabello mushrooms. They are the same size and shape as white mushrooms but are dark brown and have a meatier, firmer texture.

Roasted cauliflower "steaks" with tomato-basil vinaigrette

Serves 4

1   **head cauliflower (about 2 pounds)**
¾   **teaspoon salt**
1   **teaspoon grated lemon zest**
1   **large plum tomato, finely chopped**
¼   **cup chopped fresh basil**
2   **tablespoons rice vinegar**
2   **teaspoons extra-virgin olive oil**
1   **small garlic clove, crushed through a press**
½   **ounce shaved Parmesan**

1   Preheat oven to 375°F. Line large rimmed baking sheet with nonstick foil.

2   Trim green leaves and stem from cauliflower, leaving core intact so slices will hold together. Cut cauliflower into ¾-inch-thick slices.

3   Spray large skillet with nonstick spray and set over medium-high heat. Add cauliflower in batches and cook until browned in spots, about 3 minutes per side. Transfer to prepared baking sheet in single layer. Spray cauliflower lightly with nonstick spray. Sprinkle with ½ teaspoon of salt and the lemon zest. Bake until tender, about 20 minutes.

4   Meanwhile, stir together tomato, basil, vinegar, oil, garlic, and remaining ¼ teaspoon of salt in small bowl. Transfer cauliflower to serving platter and spoon tomato mixture over top. Sprinkle with Parmesan.

(1)   **SmartPoints value per serving** (¼ of cauliflower and about 2 tablespoons vinaigrette): 93 Cal, 4 g Total Fat, 1 g Sat Fat, 541 mg Sod, 12 g Total Carb, 6 g Sugar, 6 g Fib, 6 g Prot.

Tip
When cutting the cauliflower into slices, don't worry if some small pieces fall away from the slices. Once roasted, they will be just as delicious as the pretty cauliflower "steaks."

Orange-scented turnips and greens

Serves 4

2½	**pounds turnips (3 large), with greens attached**
2	**teaspoons olive oil**
4	**garlic cloves, thinly sliced**
1	**tablespoon white balsamic vinegar**
½	**teaspoon salt**
1	**tablespoon honey**
1	**teaspoon grated orange zest**

1 Preheat oven to 400°F. Spray large rimmed baking sheet with nonstick spray.

2 Peel turnips and cut into ¾-inch cubes. Place turnips in medium bowl; drizzle with 1 teaspoon of oil and toss to coat. Transfer to prepared baking sheet and spread in single layer. Bake, stirring once, until tender, 25–30 minutes.

3 Meanwhile, remove and discard stems from turnip greens and coarsely chop leaves. Heat remaining 1 teaspoon oil in large nonstick skillet over medium heat. Add garlic and cook, stirring constantly, until garlic just begins to turn golden, about 2 minutes. Add half of turnip greens and cook, stirring constantly, until wilted. Add remaining turnip greens and cook, stirring occasionally, until tender, about 5 minutes. Stir in vinegar and ¼ teaspoon of salt.

4 Return turnips to medium bowl; add honey, orange zest, and remaining ¼ teaspoon of salt and toss to coat. Spoon turnip greens onto serving platter, top with turnips, and serve at once.

2 **SmartPoints value per serving** (1 cup): 124 Cal, 3 g Total Fat, 0 g Sat Fat, 479 mg Sod, 25 g Total Carb, 16 g Sugar, 5 g Fib, 3 g Prot.

Tip
If you can't find turnips with the greens attached, use 1½ pounds turnip roots and 1 pound turnip, beet, collard, or mustard greens for this recipe.

Rosemary chicken with pears and leeks

Serves 4

4	**(5-ounce) skinless boneless chicken breasts**
2	**teaspoons chopped fresh rosemary**
½	**teaspoon salt**
1	**teaspoon olive oil**
2	**large firm-ripe pears, cored and thinly sliced**
2	**small leeks, cleaned and thinly sliced, white and light green parts only**
⅔	**cup dry white wine or reduced-sodium chicken broth**
1	**tablespoon white balsamic vinegar**
2	**teaspoons honey**
⅛	**teaspoon red pepper flakes**
1	**tablespoon unsalted butter**

1 Sprinkle chicken with 1 teaspoon of rosemary and ¼ teaspoon of salt. Heat ½ teaspoon of oil in large nonstick skillet over medium heat. Add chicken and cook, turning once, until lightly browned and cooked through, about 8 minutes. Transfer to plate and cover to keep warm.

2 Add remaining ½ teaspoon of oil to skillet. Arrange pears in skillet in single layer, cut side down. Add leeks to skillet and cook until pears are lightly browned on bottoms, 3 minutes.

3 Stir in wine, vinegar, honey, pepper flakes, remaining 1 teaspoon of rosemary, and remaining ¼ teaspoon salt. Cook until pears are softened and liquid has reduced by about half, 4 minutes.

4 Remove from heat and stir in butter. Serve chicken with pear mixture.

4 **SmartPoints value per serving** (1 chicken breast and ¾ cup pear mixture): 336 Cal, 8 g Total Fat, 3 g Sat Fat, 364 mg Sod, 27 g Total Carb, 16 g Sugar, 4 g Fib, 33 g Prot.

Chicken with roasted grape sauce

Serves 4

¾ **pound red seedless grapes, stems removed**

4 **(5-ounce) skinless boneless chicken breasts**

1½ **teaspoons herbes de Provence**

¼ **teaspoon salt**

⅛ **teaspoon black pepper**

1 **teaspoon unsalted butter, softened**

1 **teaspoon all-purpose flour**

1 **teaspoon olive oil**

2 **small shallots, finely chopped**

1 **cup reduced-sodium chicken broth**

½ **cup dry red wine**

1 **tablespoon chopped fresh flat-leaf parsley**

1 Preheat oven to 425°F. Spray medium rimmed baking sheet with nonstick spray.

2 Place grapes on prepared baking sheet. Bake, shaking pan once, until grapes are softened and beginning to brown in spots, about 10 minutes.

3 Meanwhile, sprinkle chicken with 1 teaspoon of herbes de Provence, salt, and pepper. Stir together butter and flour in small bowl and set aside.

4 Heat oil in large nonstick skillet over medium heat. Add chicken and cook, turning once, until browned and cooked through, 8–10 minutes. Transfer chicken to serving platter and cover to keep warm.

5 Add shallots, broth, and wine to skillet. Increase heat to medium-high and bring to boil. Cook, stirring to scrape up browned bits, until liquid is reduced to ¾ cup, 3–4 minutes. Add flour mixture and cook, whisking constantly, until sauce thickens slightly and is reduced to about ½ cup, 1–2 minutes longer. Stir in grapes, remaining ½ teaspoon herbes de Provence, and any pan juices.

6 Spoon sauce over chicken. Sprinkle with parsley and serve.

 SmartPoints value per serving (1 chicken breast and about ⅓ cup sauce): 282 Cal, 6 g Total Fat, 2 g Sat Fat, 351 mg Sod, 19 g Total Carb, 14 g Sugar, 1 g Fib, 33 g Prot.

Tip
Use the same roasting technique in this recipe to make roasted grapes for a dessert. Serve them over low-fat frozen yogurt or plain low-fat Greek yogurt.

Chicken with roasted grape sauce

Slow-cooker chicken with celery root and rosemary

Serves 4

4 (6-ounce) bone-in skinless chicken thighs, trimmed

¾ teaspoon salt

¼ teaspoon black pepper

1 large onion, chopped

1 cup reduced-sodium chicken broth

4 large garlic cloves, thinly sliced

1 celery root (1½ pounds) peeled and cut into 1-inch chunks

4 carrots, halved lengthwise and cut into 1-inch chunks

½ cup apple cider

2 teaspoons minced fresh rosemary

2 tablespoons fat-free half-and-half

1 tablespoon cornstarch

1 tablespoon Dijon mustard

1 apple, peeled, cored, and thinly sliced

Chopped flat-leaf parsley

1 Sprinkle chicken with ½ teaspoon of salt and pepper. Spray large skillet with nonstick spray and set over medium-high heat. Add chicken and cook, turning once, until browned, about 8 minutes. Transfer chicken to plate. Reduce heat to medium. Add onion to skillet and cook, covered, stirring often, until lightly browned, about 4 minutes. Add broth and garlic and bring to boil, stirring to scrape up browned bits from bottom of pan. Remove from heat.

2 Combine celery root, carrots, apple cider, rosemary, and remaining ¼ teaspoon salt in 5- to 6-quart slow cooker. Stir in onion mixture. Arrange chicken over vegetables. Cover and cook until chicken and vegetables are fork-tender, 5–6 hours on Low.

3 Whisk together half-and-half, cornstarch, and mustard in small cup until smooth. Transfer chicken to plate and cover to keep warm. Add apple to slow cooker and stir in half-and-half mixture. Cover and cook on High until mixture comes to a simmer, 25–30 minutes. Return chicken to slow cooker, cover, and cook until heated through, about 5 minutes. Sprinkle with parsley and serve.

⑤ **SmartPoints value per serving** (1 chicken thigh, 1 cup vegetables, and ⅓ cup sauce): 373 Cal, 8 g Total Fat, 2 g Sat Fat, 999 mg Sod, 39 g Total Carb, 16 g Sugar, 7 g Fib, 38 g Prot.

Tip
Celery root, also called celeriac, has an intimidating knobby exterior, but inside is a crisp celery-flavored flesh that is equally delicious served raw or cooked.

Thai turkey and broccoli stir-fry

Serves 4

3   **tablespoons reduced-sodium soy sauce**

2   **tablespoons lime juice**

1   **tablespoon Asian fish sauce**

1   **tablespoon packed brown sugar**

1½ **teaspoons canola oil**

1   **pound turkey cutlets, cut into ½-inch cubes**

1   **shallot, finely chopped**

1   **jalapeño pepper, seeded and minced**

1   **small bunch broccoli (about ¾ pound), stems trimmed and sliced, tops cut into small florets**

½   **cup water**

1   **cup shredded carrot**

⅓   **cup chopped fresh cilantro**

2   **tablespoons unsalted roasted peanuts, chopped**

1 Stir together soy sauce, lime juice, fish sauce, and brown sugar in small bowl.

2 Heat 1 teaspoon of oil in large nonstick skillet over medium heat. Add turkey and cook, stirring constantly until no longer pink, about 2 minutes. Transfer turkey to plate. Add remaining ½ teaspoon of oil to skillet. Add shallot and jalapeño and cook, stirring constantly, until fragrant, about 1 minute. Add to plate with turkey.

3 Add broccoli and water to skillet. Cook, stirring often, until broccoli is crisp-tender and water evaporates, about 3 minutes. Add carrot, turkey mixture, and soy-sauce mixture to skillet. Cook, stirring often, until turkey is heated through, about 2 minutes. Remove skillet from heat and stir in cilantro. Sprinkle with peanuts and serve.

2 | **SmartPoints value per serving** (1 ½ cups): 241 Cal, 6 g Total Fat, 1 g Sat Fat, 910 mg Sod, 16 g Total Carb, 8 g Sugar, 4 g Fib, 32 g Prot.

Tip
Accompany each serving with ⅓ cup cooked brown rice for an extra 2 SmartPoints value.

Orecchiette with
sausage and
broccoli rabe

Orecchiette with sausage and broccoli rabe

Serves 6

8   ounces orecchiette pasta

1   bunch (1¼ pounds) broccoli
     rabe, trimmed and chopped

¾   pound Italian turkey sausage,
     casing removed

2   garlic cloves, thinly sliced

½   teaspoon red pepper flakes

1   cup grape tomatoes, halved

2   tablespoons white-wine vinegar

½   teaspoon salt

6   tablespoons finely shredded
     Romano

1 Bring large pot of lightly salted water to boil. Add pasta and cook 4 minutes. Add broccoli rabe and cook until pasta and greens are just tender, about 5 minutes longer. Drain, reserving ¼ cup of cooking water.

2 Meanwhile, cook sausage in large nonstick skillet over medium heat, breaking it up with wooden spoon, until no longer pink, about 4 minutes. Add garlic and red pepper flakes and cook, stirring constantly, until fragrant, 30 seconds. Add tomatoes, reserved cooking water, vinegar, and salt and cook, stirring to scrape up browned bits from bottom of pan, just until tomatoes are heated through, about 1 minute.

3 Add pasta mixture to skillet and stir to combine. Divide pasta evenly among 6 bowls. Sprinkle evenly with Romano and serve.

7 **SmartPoints value per serving** (generous 1 cup pasta mixture and 1 tablespoon cheese): 267 Cal, 7 g Total Fat, 3 g Sat Fat, 669 mg Sod, 33 g Total Carb, 2 g Sugar, 4 g Fib, 18 g Prot.

Tip
Broccoli rabe, also called rapini, looks like leafy broccoli. It is sturdier than regular broccoli and has a slightly bitter flavor. To prepare it, trim away the large tough stems, leaving the slender stems, leaves, and florets.

Grilled coffee-rubbed steak with pear-cranberry salsa

Serves 4

1	**tablespoon ground coffee**
2	**teaspoons packed brown sugar**
1	**teaspoon ground cumin**
1	**teaspoon salt**
½	**teaspoon black pepper**
½	**teaspoon chipotle chile powder**
1	**pound lean sirloin steak, trimmed (about 1 inch thick)**
2	**large firm-ripe pears, cored and diced**
¼	**cup dried cranberries**
3	**tablespoons diced red onion**
2	**tablespoons chopped fresh cilantro**
2	**tablespoons lime juice**
1	**jalapeño pepper, seeded and minced**

1 Spray grill rack with nonstick spray. Preheat grill to medium-high or prepare medium-high fire.

2 Stir together coffee, brown sugar, cumin, ¾ teaspoon of salt, black pepper, and chile powder in small bowl. Rub coffee mixture all over steak and let stand at room temperature 15 minutes.

3 Meanwhile, to make salsa, combine pears, cranberries, onion, cilantro, lime juice, jalapeño, and remaining ¼ teaspoon salt in small bowl.

4 Place steak on grill rack and grill, turning occasionally, until instant-read thermometer inserted into side of steak registers 145°F, about 10 minutes. Transfer steak to cutting board and let stand 5 minutes. Cut steak into 24 slices. Serve steak with salsa.

5 **SmartPoints value per serving** (6 slices steak and about ⅔ cup salsa): 256 Cal, 4 g Total Fat, 2 g Sat Fat, 659 mg Sod, 29 g Total Carb, 20 g Sugar, 4 g Fib, 26 g Prot.

Tip
To make the salsa more colorful, choose a green pear, such as Bartlett or Anjou, along with a red pear, such as Red Anjou or Starkrimson.

Grilled coffee-rubbed steak with pear-cranberry salsa

Beef, cauliflower, and edamame curry

Serves 4

1	**cup frozen shelled edamame**
½	**large head cauliflower (about 2 pounds), cut into bite-size pieces**
1	**cup light (low-fat) coconut milk**
½	**cup water**
4	**teaspoons red curry paste or more to taste**
1	**tablespoon red-wine vinegar**
1	**tablespoon all-purpose flour**
2	**garlic cloves, minced**
2	**teaspoons grated peeled fresh ginger**
1	**teaspoon salt**
2	**teaspoons canola oil**
½	**pound lean sirloin, trimmed and thinly sliced**
1	**onion, halved and thinly sliced**
1	**small red bell pepper, diced**

Chopped fresh cilantro

Lime wedges

1 Bring large saucepan of lightly salted water to boil. Add edamame and cauliflower, return to boil, and cook just until crisp-tender, about 3 minutes. Drain.

2 Whisk together coconut milk, water, curry paste, vinegar, flour, garlic, ginger, and ½ teaspoon of salt in medium bowl until smooth.

3 Heat 1 teaspoon of oil in large skillet over medium-high heat. Sprinkle beef with remaining ½ teaspoon of salt. Add beef to skillet and cook, stirring often, just until browned, about 2 minutes. Transfer to plate.

4 Add remaining 1 teaspoon of oil to skillet. Add onion and bell pepper and cook, stirring often, until crisp-tender, about 3 minutes.

5 Rewhisk coconut milk mixture and add to skillet. Add beef and cauliflower mixture, and cook, stirring constantly, until sauce comes to boil and thickens, about 1 minute. Sprinkle each serving with cilantro and serve with lime wedges.

5   **SmartPoints value per serving** (1¾ cups): 286 Cal, 11 g Total Fat, 3 g Sat Fat, 780 mg Sod, 27 g Total Carb, 10 g Sugar, 8 g Fib, 23 g Prot.

Tip
Serve each portion of the stir-fry with ⅓ cup cooked brown basmati rice for an additional 2 SmartPoints value.

Slow-cooker lamb, chickpea, and squash stew

Serves 4

1	**pound lean leg of lamb, trimmed and cut into 1-inch pieces**
¾	**teaspoon salt**
1	**onion, chopped**
4	**garlic cloves, minced**
2	**teaspoons ground cumin**
1½	**teaspoons paprika**
1	**teaspoon ground coriander**
½	**teaspoon ground ginger**
⅛	**teaspoon cayenne**
2	**cups reduced-sodium chicken broth**
4	**plum tomatoes, cut into 1-inch chunks**
1	**(15½-ounce) can chickpeas, rinsed and drained**
2	**pounds kabocha squash, peeled, seeded, and cut into 1½-inch chunks**
2	**tablespoons chopped fresh cilantro**

1 Spray large skillet with nonstick spray and set over medium-high heat. Sprinkle lamb with ½ teaspoon salt. Add half of lamb to skillet and cook, stirring often, until lamb is browned, about 5 minutes. Transfer to 5- to 6-quart slow cooker. Repeat with remaining lamb.

2 Add onion, garlic, cumin, paprika, coriander, ginger, remaining ¼ teaspoon salt, and cayenne to skillet and cook, stirring constantly, until onion begins to soften, 2 minutes. Add broth to skillet and cook, stirring to scrape up browned bits, about 1 minute. Add broth mixture to slow cooker.

3 Add tomatoes and chickpeas to slow cooker and stir to combine. Arrange squash over top in even layer. Cover and cook on High 4–5 hours or Low 8–10 hours. Serve sprinkled with cilantro.

3 **SmartPoints value per serving** (2 cups): 343 Cal, 7 g Total Fat, 2 g Sat Fat, 960 mg Sod, 42 g Total Carb, 10 g Sugar, 10 g Fib, 33 g Prot.

Tip
Kabocha squash are small, squat, round squash with a stippled green or orange exterior. The flesh is thick and dark orange and cooks up with a creamy texture. If you can't find it, use butternut squash in this recipe.

Pork tenderloin
with lentils and
winter squash

Pork tenderloin with lentils and winter squash

Serves 6

1½ **pounds lean pork tenderloin, trimmed**

2 **tablespoons Dijon mustard**

¼ **cup panko bread crumbs**

2 **tablespoons grated Parmesan cheese**

1 **tablespoon olive oil**

1 **large red onion, chopped**

2 **garlic cloves, minced**

⅔ **cup brown lentils, picked over and rinsed**

1¾ **cups chicken broth**

4 **cups peeled, seeded, and diced butternut, Kabocha, or Hubbard squash**

2 **tablespoons white balsamic vinegar**

1 **tablespoon minced fresh rosemary**

1½ **teaspoons salt**

¼ **teaspoon black pepper**

1 Preheat oven to 425°F. Line medium baking sheet with parchment paper.

2 Place pork on baking sheet and brush all over with mustard. Stir together panko and Parmesan in small bowl. Sprinkle on pork, pressing to adhere and rolling to coat on all sides. Lightly spray pork with olive oil nonstick spray. Bake until instant-read thermometer inserted in center of pork reads 145°F, about 25 minutes. Let stand 10 minutes. Cut into 18 slices.

3 Meanwhile, heat oil in large nonstick skillet over medium heat. Add onion and cook, stirring often, until softened, 5 minutes. Add garlic and cook, stirring constantly, until fragrant, 30 seconds. Add lentils and broth and bring to boil. Reduce heat, and simmer, covered, 12 minutes. Scatter squash over lentils in even layer. Cover and cook until lentils and squash are tender, about 12 minutes longer. Stir in vinegar, rosemary, salt, and pepper. Serve pork with lentil mixture.

4 **SmartPoints value per serving** (3 slices pork and 1 cup lentil mixture): 314 Cal, 6 g Total Fat, 2 g Sat Fat, 1,077 mg Sod, 32 g Total Carb, 6 g Sugar, 5 g Fib, 32 g Prot.

Stuffed pork chops with creamy mustard sauce

Serves 4

1   cup chopped red onion
2   large garlic cloves, minced
1   (¾-pound) bunch Swiss chard, tough stems removed, leaves chopped
1   tablespoon water
3   tablespoons dried tart cherries, chopped
½   plus ⅛ teaspoon salt
4   (8-ounce) lean boneless pork chops, trimmed (1-inch thick)
¾   cup reduced-sodium chicken broth
¼   teaspoon dried thyme
3   tablespoons fat-free half-and-half
2   teaspoons Dijon mustard
1   teaspoon cornstarch

1 Preheat oven to 375°F. Line medium rimmed baking sheet with foil.

2 Spray large skillet with nonstick spray and set over medium heat. Add onion and cook, stirring often, until softened, 5 minutes. Add garlic and cook, stirring, until fragrant, 30 seconds. Add Swiss chard and water and cook, stirring often, until chard is tender, about 3 minutes. Stir in cherries and ¼ teaspoon of salt. Transfer vegetable mixture to plate to cool.

3 Make pocket in each pork chop by inserting small sharp knife into side of chop and cutting back and forth until large, deep pocket is formed. Fill each pocket evenly with vegetable mixture. Secure stuffing with wooden toothpicks. Sprinkle chops on both sides with ¼ teaspoon of remaining salt.

4 Wipe out skillet and spray with nonstick spray. Set over medium heat. Add chops and cook, turning once, until browned, about 8 minutes. Transfer chops to prepared baking sheet (do not wash skillet). Bake until instant-read thermometer inserted into thickest part of chops registers 145°F, about 12 minutes.

5 When chops are almost done, return skillet to medium heat. Add broth and thyme and bring to boil, stirring to scrape up browned bits in skillet. Boil until reduced to ½ cup, about 2 minutes. Whisk together half-and-half, mustard, and cornstarch in small bowl; add to skillet, whisking constantly. Simmer, whisking constantly, until sauce is thickened, about 2 minutes. Stir in remaining ⅛ teaspoon salt and any accumulated juices from baking sheet. Remove toothpicks from chops and serve with sauce.

 SmartPoints value per serving (1 chop and 1 generous tablespoon sauce): 396 Cal, 13 g Total Fat, 4 g Sat Fat, 835 mg Sod, 16 g Total Carb, 10 g Sugar, 3 g Fib, 51 g Prot.

Tip
Instead of the Swiss chard, you can use mustard greens or kale for this recipe. These greens tend to be sturdier, so you may need to cook them a few minutes longer in step 2, adding additional water if needed.

Stuffed pork chops with
creamy mustard sauce

Dijon-roasted salmon with fall vegetables

Dijon-roasted salmon with fall vegetables

Serves 4

1 teaspoon whole cumin seeds

4 teaspoons packed brown sugar

2 tablespoons whole-grain Dijon mustard

4 (6-ounce) skinless salmon fillets

1 teaspoon olive oil

1 onion, halved and thinly sliced

¼ head Savoy cabbage, thinly sliced (4 cups)

¼ pound kale, stems removed, leaves thinly sliced (4 cups)

1 cup shredded carrot

¼ cup chicken broth

1 tablespoon grated peeled fresh ginger

¾ teaspoon salt

Lime wedges

1 Preheat oven to 450°F. Spray medium rimmed baking sheet with nonstick spray.

2 Place cumin seeds in small dry skillet and set over medium heat. Cook, shaking pan often, until seeds are fragrant and lightly toasted, about 3 minutes. Transfer to plate to cool.

3 Stir together brown sugar and mustard in small bowl. Place salmon on prepared baking sheet. Top evenly with brown-sugar mixture. Bake until salmon is just opaque in center, 10–12 minutes.

4 Meanwhile, heat oil in large deep nonstick skillet over medium heat. Add onion and cook, stirring occasionally, until golden brown, about 8 minutes. Add cabbage, kale, carrot, broth, ginger, salt, and cumin seeds. Cook, stirring often, until vegetables are crisp-tender and water evaporates, about 5 minutes.

5 Spoon vegetable mixture evenly onto 4 plates and top each with 1 salmon filet. Serve with lime wedges.

2 **SmartPoints value per serving** (1 salmon fillet and about 1 cup vegetables): 446 Cal, 25 g Total Fat, 5 g Sat Fat, 819 mg Sod, 17 g Total Carb, 9 g Sugar, 5 g Fib, 38 g Prot.

Tip
Savoy cabbage looks like regular green cabbage, but the leaves are deeply wrinkled and it has a milder, sweeter flavor.

Ginger shrimp with soba-spinach sauté

Serves 4

4   ounces soba noodles

⅔   cup ponzu sauce

3   scallions, thinly sliced, plus additional for garnish

4   teaspoons minced peeled fresh ginger

3   large garlic cloves, minced

1   teaspoon Asian (dark) sesame oil

1   pound large peeled and deveined shrimp

½   red bell pepper, very thinly sliced

1   (10-ounce) bag fresh spinach, chopped

1 Preheat broiler.

2 Cook soba noodles according to package directions. Set aside.

3 Stir together ponzu sauce, scallions, 2 teaspoons of ginger, 1 teaspoon of garlic, and the sesame oil in medium bowl. Add shrimp and toss to coat. Transfer shrimp mixture to large flameproof baking pan and spread in even layer. Broil 6 inches from heat until shrimp are just opaque in center, about 3 minutes.

4 Meanwhile, spray large skillet with nonstick spray and set over medium-high heat. Add bell pepper and cook, stirring often, until crisp-tender, about 3 minutes. Add remaining 2 teaspoons of ginger and remaining garlic and cook, stirring constantly, until fragrant, 30 seconds. Add spinach in batches and cook, stirring constantly until wilted, about 2 minutes. Stir in soba noodles. Divide soba mixture among 4 plates and top with shrimp. Drizzle pan juices over shrimp and garnish with thinly sliced scallions.

(4) **SmartPoints value per serving** (1¼ cups noodle mixture and about 8 shrimp): 236 Cal, 3 g Total Fat, 1 g Sat Fat, 1,736 mg Sod, 32 g Total Carb, 3 g Sugar, 2 g Fib, 23 g Prot.

Tip
Ponzu sauce is a sweet and tangy combination of soy sauce, lemon juice, and sugar. Look for it in the Asian section of your supermarket.

Ginger shrimp with
soba-spinach sauté

Black bean, farro, and roasted squash chili

Black bean, farro, and roasted squash chili

Serves 6

3   cups (¾-inch) cubes peeled seeded butternut squash

2   poblano peppers, diced

1   onion, chopped

4   garlic cloves, minced

2   tablespoons chili powder

1   tablespoon ground cumin

1   teaspoon salt

½   teaspoon chipotle chile powder

1   (28-ounce) can petite diced tomatoes

1   (15½-ounce) can black beans, rinsed and drained

1   cup frozen corn kernels

1½   cups reduced-sodium vegetable broth

1   cup cooked farro

6   tablespoons light sour cream

6   tablespoons shredded reduced-fat Cheddar cheese

1 Preheat oven to 400°F. Line rimmed baking sheet with foil and spray foil with nonstick spray.

2 Spread squash on half of baking sheet and poblano peppers on other half. Lightly spray vegetables with nonstick spray. Bake, stirring once, until peppers are tender, about 25 minutes. Transfer peppers to plate. Spread out squash and return to oven. Bake until squash is tender, about 10 minutes longer.

3 Spray Dutch oven with nonstick spray and set over medium-high heat. Add onion and cook, stirring often, until onion begins to brown, 6 minutes. Stir in garlic, chili powder, cumin, salt, and chipotle chile powder and cook, stirring constantly, until fragrant, 30 seconds. Add tomatoes, beans, corn, broth, and roasted poblano peppers to Dutch oven and bring to boil. Reduce heat and simmer, covered, 30 minutes. Stir in squash and farro and simmer until heated through, 3 minutes. Serve topped with sour cream and Cheddar.

3   **SmartPoints value per serving** (about 1⅓ cups chili, 1 tablespoon sour cream, and 1 tablespoon cheese): 247 Cal, 4 g Total Fat, 2 g Sat Fat, 1,057 mg Sod, 47 g Total Carb, 9 g Sugar, 11 g Fib, 12 g Prot.

Tip

To get 1 cup cooked farro, cook ½ cup dry farro in 2 cups lightly salted water until tender, about 25 minutes; then drain. Make extra farro and serve it instead of rice as a side dish with another meal (⅓ cup cooked farro has 2 SmartPoints value).

Red curry tofu and vegetable bowls

Serves 6

1	**(14-ounce) package reduced-fat firm tofu, cut into ¾-inch cubes**
2	**teaspoons canola oil**
1	**red onion, chopped**
1	**tablespoon red curry paste**
3	**garlic cloves, minced**
2	**teaspoons grated peeled fresh ginger**
1	**(14½-ounce) can diced tomatoes**
1	**cup light (low-fat) coconut milk**
1	**tablespoon packed brown sugar**
½	**head cauliflower, cut into small florets (about 3 cups)**
2	**carrots, thinly sliced**
1	**apple, peeled, cored, and diced**
½	**teaspoon salt**
1	**cup loosely packed fresh cilantro leaves**
	Lime wedges

1 Place tofu between layers of paper towels and let drain 15 minutes, pressing occasionally.

2 Heat oil in large nonstick skillet over medium heat. Add tofu and cook, turning once, until browned, about 6 minutes. Transfer tofu to plate.

3 Add onion to skillet and cook, stirring often, until softened, 5 minutes. Add curry paste, garlic, and ginger and cook, stirring constantly, until fragrant, 30 seconds. Stir in tomatoes, coconut milk, and brown sugar. Bring to boil. Stir in cauliflower, carrots, apple, and salt. Return to boil, reduce heat and simmer, covered, until vegetables are crisp-tender, about 8 minutes. Stir in tofu; cover and simmer until tofu is heated through, about 2 minutes. Remove from heat and stir in cilantro. Serve with lime wedges.

3 **SmartPoints value per serving** (1 cup): 149 Cal, 6 g Total Fat, 2 g Sat Fat, 392 mg Sod, 21 g Total Carb, 11 g Sugar, 5 g Fib, 8 g Prot.

Tip
For an additional 3 SmartPoints value, spoon each serving of the curry over ½ cup cooked rice noodles.

Cranberry-almond cupcakes

Makes 12

1½ cups all-purpose flour

1½ teaspoons baking powder

¼ teaspoon baking soda

¼ teaspoon salt

½ cup low-fat buttermilk

1 teaspoon vanilla extract

¼ teaspoon almond extract

5 tablespoons unsalted butter, softened

1 cup sugar

2 large egg whites

1 large egg

¾ cup fresh or frozen cranberries, coarsely chopped

⅓ cup mini–semisweet chocolate chips

¼ cup sliced almonds

1 Preheat oven to 350°F. Line 12-cup muffin pan with paper liners.

2 Whisk together flour, baking powder, baking soda, and salt in medium bowl. Combine buttermilk, vanilla, and almond extract in small bowl.

3 With electric mixer on low speed, beat butter in large bowl until creamy. Gradually beat in sugar. Increase speed to medium and beat 3 minutes. Gradually beat in egg whites and egg. With mixer on low speed, beat in flour mixture alternately with buttermilk mixture, beginning and ending with flour mixture, beating until batter is smooth. Stir in cranberries and chocolate chips.

4 Spoon batter into prepared muffin cups. Sprinkle with almonds. Bake until toothpick inserted in centers of cupcakes comes out clean, 20–25 minutes. Let cupcakes cool in pan on wire rack 10 minutes. Remove cupcakes from pan and cool completely on rack.

9 **SmartPoints value per serving** (1 cupcake): 215 Cal, 8 g Total Fat, 4 g Sat Fat, 167 mg Sod, 34 g Total Carb, 20 g Sugar, 1 g Fib, 4 g Prot.

Tip
Cranberries are also known as "bounce berries." If you try to chop them on a cutting board, you'll soon see how they got the name! To make the task of chopping them easier, place cranberries in a food processor and pulse a couple of times.

Carrot-apple Bundt cake with cream cheese glaze

Serves 24

Cake

2½	cups all-purpose flour
2½	teaspoons baking powder
2	teaspoons cinnamon
½	teaspoon baking soda
½	teaspoon salt
1	cup granulated sugar
¾	cup packed brown sugar
3	large eggs
⅓	cup canola oil
1	tablespoon vanilla extract
¾	pound carrots, shredded
1	apple, peeled, cored, and diced
½	cup dried cranberries

Glaze

1¼	cups confectioners' sugar
2	tablespoons light cream cheese, softened (Neufchâtel)
1	tablespoon plus 1 teaspoon low-fat (1%) milk
⅛	teaspoon vanilla extract

1 Preheat oven to 350°F. Spray 10-inch Bundt pan with nonstick baking spray.

2 To make cake, whisk together flour, baking powder, cinnamon, baking soda, and salt in medium bowl.

3 With electric mixer on medium speed, beat granulated sugar, brown sugar, and eggs in large bowl until thickened, 2 minutes. Add oil and vanilla and beat until blended. With mixer on low speed, beat in flour mixture just until blended (batter will be thick). Add carrots, apple, and cranberries and stir just until blended.

4 Spoon batter into prepared pan and smooth top. Bake until toothpick inserted into center of cake comes out clean, 45–50 minutes. Let cake cool in pan on rack for 10 minutes. Remove cake from pan and let cool completely on rack.

5 To make glaze, with electric mixer on low speed, beat confectioners' sugar, cream cheese, 1 tablespoon of milk, and vanilla until blended. Increase speed to medium and beat until smooth. Beat in additional 1 teaspoon milk if needed. Drizzle glaze over cooled cake.

8 **SmartPoints value per serving** (1⁄24 of cake): 192 Cal, 4 g Total Fat, 1 g Sat Fat, 152 mg Sod, 37 g Total Carb, 25 g Sugar, 1 g Fib, 2 g Prot.

Carrot-apple Bundt cake
with cream cheese glaze

Butternut squash
tart with
candied pecans

Butternut squash tart with candied pecans

Serves 16

1 (2½-pound) butternut squash, halved lengthwise and seeded

1 refrigerated pie crust (from 14.1-ounce package)

¾ cup fat-free egg substitute

½ cup fat-free sweetened condensed milk

⅓ cup plus 2 tablespoons packed brown sugar

½ teaspoon cinnamon

½ teaspoon ground ginger

½ cup pecan halves

1 teaspoon water

1 cup thawed frozen fat-free whipped topping

1 Preheat oven to 425°F. Line rimmed baking sheet with foil and spray foil with nonstick spray.

2 Place squash halves cut sides down on prepared baking sheet. Bake until tender, about 1 hour. Let cool. Maintain oven temperature.

3 Unroll pie crust onto floured surface and with floured rolling pin roll to 12-inch circle. Place crust in 10-inch tart pan with removable bottom. Gently press into bottom and against side of pan. Fold edge of crust into pan and press to make it even with rim. Place tart pan on prepared baking sheet and bake until crust is set and lightly browned, about 10 minutes. Let cool completely on wire rack. Reduce oven to 350°F.

4 Scoop flesh from squash and discard skin. Place squash in food processor and puree. Measure 2 cups squash and transfer to medium bowl. (Save any remaining squash for another use.)

5 Add egg substitute, condensed milk, ⅓ cup of brown sugar, cinnamon, and ginger to squash and whisk until smooth. Place tart pan on baking sheet and pour filling into crust. Bake until filling is set, about 35 minutes. Place tart on rack to cool completely. Maintain oven temperature.

6 Line small baking sheet with foil and spray foil with nonstick spray. Combine pecans, remaining 2 tablespoons brown sugar, and water in small bowl and toss to coat. Spread in single layer on prepared baking sheet. Bake until pecans are toasted, about 10 minutes. Let cool. Coarsely chop pecans. Sprinkle tart with pecans just before serving. Cut into 16 slices and top each one with 1 tablespoon whipped topping.

6 **SmartPoints value per serving** (¹⁄₁₆ of tart): 181 Cal, 6 g Total Fat, 2 g Sat Fat, 98 mg Sod, 30 g Total Carb, 15 g Sugar, 2 g Fib, 3 g Prot.

Tip
You can bake the crust and make the filling and candied pecans a day ahead. Store the crust in a zip-close plastic bag, cover and refrigerate the filling, and store the pecans in an airtight container. Bake the tart an additional 15 minutes.

Apple streusel crostata

Serves 12

⅓ cup plus 1 tablespoon all-purpose flour

1 tablespoon unsalted butter, cut into small pieces

⅓ cup packed brown sugar

¼ cup old-fashioned oats

1 tablespoon canola oil

¾ teaspoon cinnamon

4 large apples, peeled, cored, and sliced (about 2 pounds)

⅓ cup dried tart cherries

¼ cup granulated sugar

1 refrigerated pie crust (from 14.1-ounce package)

1 Preheat oven to 375°F. Line large baking sheet with parchment paper.

2 To make streusel, with your fingers, rub together ⅓ cup of flour and the butter in small bowl until small crumbs form. Stir in brown sugar, oats, oil, and cinnamon.

3 Combine apples, cherries, granulated sugar, and remaining 1 tablespoon flour in large bowl and toss to coat. Unroll crust onto prepared baking sheet. Mound apple mixture on crust, leaving 1½-inch border. Sprinkle streusel evenly over apple mixture. Fold rim of crust over to partially cover filling, pleating and pressing lightly.

4 Bake until apples are tender when pierced with tip of paring knife, 50–55 minutes. Cool 10 minutes on baking sheet on rack. Slide tart on parchment paper onto wire rack to cool completely.

8 **SmartPoints value per serving** (1/12 of tart): 219 Cal, 7 g Total Fat, 3 g Sat Fat, 81 mg Sod, 39 g Total Carb, 22 g Sugar, 3 g Fib, 2 g Prot.

Tip
Use a variety of apples to give the crostata more complex flavor. Try any combination of Granny Smith, Golden Delicious, Pink Lady, Honeycrisp, Rome, or Cortland apples.

Baked ricotta puddings with grapes

Serves 6

1½ cups part-skim ricotta
4 tablespoons sugar
2 tablespoons all-purpose flour
1 large egg, separated
½ teaspoon grated lemon zest
½ teaspoon vanilla extract
1 large egg white
⅓ cup Concord grape spreadable fruit
½ pound red or green seedless grapes, removed from stems

1 Preheat oven to 350°F. Spray 6 (6-ounce) ramekins or custard cups with nonstick spray.

2 Combine ricotta, 2 tablespoons of sugar, the flour, egg yolk, lemon zest, and vanilla in food processor; puree. Transfer to large bowl.

3 With electric mixer on medium-high speed, beat egg whites in medium bowl until soft peaks form. Gradually beat in remaining 2 tablespoons sugar, beating until stiff peaks form.

4 Gently fold egg whites into ricotta mixture in three additions, until no streaks of white remain. Spoon evenly into prepared ramekins. Place ramekins in shallow baking pan and place in oven. Fill pan with enough boiling water to come halfway up sides of ramekins. Bake until puffed and golden, about 30 minutes. Place baking pan on wire rack and let puddings cool slightly.

5 Just before serving, place spreadable fruit in medium microwaveable bowl. Microwave on High until melted, about 1 minute. Stir in grapes and microwave on High until grapes are warm, about 1 minute.

6 Spoon grape mixture over puddings and serve at once.

7 **SmartPoints value per serving** (1 pudding and about 2 tablespoons grapes): 203 Cal, 6 g Total Fat, 3 g Sat Fat, 82 mg Sod, 29 g Total Carb, 23 g Sugar, 0 g Fib, 9 g Prot.

Sweet potato–spice truffles

Makes 48

1	**medium sweet potato (about ½ pound)**
¼	**cup whole blanched almonds, toasted**
6	**pitted medjool dates (½ cup)**
⅔	**cup quick-cooking oats**
2	**tablespoons packed dark brown sugar**
½	**teaspoon pumpkin pie spice**
¼	**cup unsweetened shredded coconut, toasted**

1 Preheat oven to 400°F. Line small baking pan with foil.

2 Prick sweet potato several times with knife and place in prepared pan. Bake until tender, about 1 hour. Cut in half lengthwise and let cool completely. Remove flesh and discard peel.

3 Finely chop almonds in food processor. Remove and set aside 2 tablespoons of almonds. Add dates to food processor and puree. Add sweet potato, ⅓ cup of oats, brown sugar, and pie spice and puree. Scrape potato mixture into small bowl and stir in remaining ⅓ cup oats. Cover and refrigerate 2 hours.

4 Combine reserved 2 tablespoons almonds and coconut on plate. Shape sweet-potato mixture by rounded measuring teaspoonfuls into ¾-inch balls. Roll in coconut mixture. Store in covered container in refrigerator up to 4 days. Serve chilled.

3 **SmartPoints value per serving** (3 truffles): 64 Cal, 2 g Total Fat, 1 g Sat Fat, 8 mg Sod, 10 g Total Carb, 4 g Sugar, 1 g Fib, 1 g Prot.

Sweet potato–
spice truffles

↓ Cranberries

↓ Red onions

↓ Kale

Beets
←

Onions →

Chapter 4
Winter

Gather for cozy meals with hearty vegetables and bright citrus.

Pears
←

Kumquats
←

Rutabagas
→

Radicchio
↓

↑ Pomegranates

In this chapter

What's in season

- Apples
- Beets
- Blood oranges
- Broccoli
- Broccoli rabe
- Brussels sprouts
- Butternut squash
- Cabbage
- Carrots
- Cauliflower
- Collard greens
- Cranberries
- Kale
- Kumquats
- Leeks
- Mustard greens
- Onions
- Oranges
- Papaya
- Parsnips
- Pears
- Pomegranates
- Radicchio
- Rutabaga
- Spaghetti squash
- Spinach
- Sweet potatoes
- Tropical fruit

Frittata with Brussels sprouts and bacon

Serves 4

2   slices turkey bacon, cut into ½-inch pieces

2   teaspoons olive oil

1   red onion, thinly sliced

2   garlic cloves, finely chopped

¾   pound fresh Brussels sprouts, trimmed and thinly sliced

½   teaspoon salt

¼   teaspoon black pepper

1   (16-ounce) container fat-free egg substitute

½   cup crumbled reduced-fat goat cheese

1 Preheat broiler.

2 Place bacon in 12-inch ovenproof nonstick skillet and set over medium heat. Cook, stirring occasionally, until crisp, about 3 minutes. With slotted spoon, transfer bacon to a paper towel–lined plate. Wipe out skillet.

3 Add oil to same skillet. Add onion and cook, stirring occasionally, until softened, 5 minutes. Add garlic and cook, stirring frequently, until fragrant, 30 seconds. Add Brussels sprouts, salt, and pepper and cook, covered, stirring occasionally, until sprouts are crisp-tender and lightly browned, about 5 minutes.

4 Meanwhile, stir together egg substitute, ¼ cup of goat cheese, and bacon in medium bowl. Pour egg substitute mixture evenly over vegetable mixture. Reduce heat to medium-low and cook, covered, without stirring, until eggs are almost set, about 10 minutes.

5 Sprinkle frittata with remaining ¼ cup of cheese. Place skillet in broiler 5 inches from heat and broil until frittata is set and top is golden, about 2 minutes. Cut into 4 wedges.

3 **SmartPoints value per serving** (1 wedge): 191 Cal, 8 g Total Fat, 3 g Sat Fat, 621 mg Sod, 13 g Total Carb, 5 g Sugar, 4 g Fib, 19 g Prot.

Tip
Cook Brussels sprouts only until they are crisp-tender and still retain their green color. Overcooking gives them an unappealing soggy texture and accentuates their cabbage-like flavor.

Egg, bacon, and greens breakfast sandwiches

Serves 4

2   teaspoons olive oil

1   shallot, thinly sliced

½   pound collard greens, trimmed and thinly sliced (about 6 cups)

¼   teaspoon salt

¼   teaspoon hot sauce

2   slices turkey bacon

4   large eggs

2   whole wheat bread thins, split and toasted

2   tablespoons grated pecorino Romano

1 Heat 1 teaspoon of oil in large skillet over medium-high heat. Add shallot and cook, stirring constantly, until softened, about 2 minutes. Add greens and salt; cook, stirring frequently, until greens are tender, about 4 minutes. Stir in hot sauce. Cover and keep warm.

2 Meanwhile, place bacon in large nonstick skillet and set over medium heat. Cook until crisp, about 3 minutes on each side. With tongs, transfer bacon to a paper towel–lined plate and drain.

3 Add remaining 1 teaspoon of oil to same skillet. Break eggs into skillet and cook until whites are opaque and yolks begin to set, 3–4 minutes.

4 Place bread thin half, cut side up, on each of 4 plates. Top evenly with greens mixture. Break each slice of bacon in half and place on greens. Place an egg on top of bacon, sprinkle with pecorino, and serve at once.

3 **SmartPoints value per serving** (1 open-face sandwich): 194 Cal, 10 g Total Fat, 3 g Sat Fat, 459 mg Sod, 15 g Total Carb, 3 g Sugar, 5 g Fib, 12 g Prot.

Tip

To quickly trim collard greens, fold each leaf in half at the stem, then tear off the tough portion of the stem and discard.

Egg, bacon, and greens breakfast sandwiches

**Buttermilk waffles
with oranges and pomegranate**

Buttermilk waffles with oranges and pomegranate

Serves 8

2 cups white whole wheat flour

½ cup honey-toasted wheat germ

3 tablespoons sugar

1½ teaspoons baking powder

½ teaspoon baking soda

½ teaspoon salt

2 cups low-fat buttermilk

½ cup fat-free egg substitute

1 tablespoon canola oil

2 teaspoons grated orange zest

1 teaspoon vanilla extract

2 large oranges

1 cup pomegranate arils (from 1 pomegranate)

4 tablespoons pure maple syrup, warmed

1 Spray Belgian waffle–maker with nonstick spray. Preheat according to manufacturer's instructions.

2 Whisk together flour, wheat germ, sugar, baking powder, baking soda, and salt in large bowl. Whisk together buttermilk, egg substitute, oil, orange zest, and vanilla in medium bowl. Add buttermilk mixture to flour mixture and stir until moistened.

3 Scoop 1⅓ cups batter for 2 (4½-inch) square waffles into waffle maker; lightly spread batter to fill each grid. Close lid and bake until golden brown, about 4 minutes. Transfer waffles to platter and keep warm. Repeat with remaining batter, spraying waffle maker between batches, making total of 8 waffles.

4 With sharp knife, cut off slice from top and bottom of oranges. Stand fruit upright. Cut off peel and white pith, cutting from top to bottom, turning fruit as you go. Cut oranges crosswise into ½-inch rounds; cut rounds in half.

5 Top waffles evenly with oranges and pomegranate arils. Serve with maple syrup.

 SmartPoints value per serving (1 waffle with ¼ cup orange segments, 2 tablespoons arils, ½ tablespoon maple syrup): 273 Cal, 4 g Total Fat, 1 g Sat Fat, 439 mg Sod, 49 g Total Carb, 25 g Sugar, 3 g Fib, 10 g Prot.

Tip

To prep a pomegranate, cut off and discard the top; then cut into 4 wedges. Place one wedge at a time in a large bowl of cool water. Hold the wedge underwater and use your fingers to gently remove the arils. Discard peel and pith, and drain off water.

Almond breakfast quinoa with kumquats

Serves 4

1　**cup quinoa, rinsed**

1½　**cups unsweetened almond milk**

1　**(1-inch) piece fresh ginger, smashed**

2　**tablespoons sugar**

¼　**teaspoon salt**

12　**kumquats, thinly sliced and seeded**

1 Place quinoa in small saucepan and set over medium-high heat. Cook, stirring frequently, until fragrant, about 5 minutes. Stir in almond milk, ginger, sugar, and salt and bring to boil. Reduce heat and simmer, covered, until most of liquid is absorbed and quinoa is tender, 20–25 minutes.

2 Remove and discard ginger. Divide quinoa among 4 bowls; top evenly with kumquats.

6 **SmartPoints value per serving** (about ½ cup quinoa with about 3 tablespoons kumquats): 237 Cal, 4 g Total Fat, 0 g Sat Fat, 208 mg Sod, 44 g Total Carb, 12 g Sugar, 7 g Fib, 8 g Prot.

Tip
Go ahead and eat the whole thing! Kumquats are meant to be eaten, skin and all. They brighten up dishes with their sweet-tart citrus flavor and vibrant color. If they are unavailable, top the quinoa with orange segments.

**Almond breakfast
quinoa with kumquats**

Apple-cranberry muffins

Serves 12

Streusel

2	**tablespoons all-purpose flour**
2	**tablespoons packed light brown sugar**
1	**tablespoon cold unsalted butter, cut into small pieces**
2	**tablespoons chopped toasted walnuts**

Muffins

¾	**cup fresh or frozen cranberries**
1	**cup all-purpose flour**
1	**cup whole wheat flour**
2	**teaspoons baking powder**
½	**teaspoon baking soda**
¾	**teaspoon cinnamon**
¼	**teaspoon salt**
¾	**cup fat-free plain Greek yogurt**
½	**cup fat-free milk**
¼	**cup canola oil**
½	**cup granulated sugar**
1	**large egg**
1	**teaspoon vanilla extract**
1	**small apple, peeled and finely chopped (½ cup)**

1 Preheat oven to 375°F. Line 12-cup muffin pan with paper liners; spray liners with nonstick spray.

2 To make streusel, stir together flour and brown sugar in small bowl. Add butter and use fingers to blend butter into flour until mixture resembles coarse crumbs. Stir in walnuts. Set aside.

3 To make muffins, place cranberries in food processor; pulse until coarsely chopped, 3-4 times. Set aside.

4 Whisk together all-purpose flour, whole wheat flour, baking powder, baking soda, cinnamon, and salt in large bowl. Whisk together yogurt, milk, oil, sugar, egg, and vanilla in medium bowl.

5 Add yogurt mixture, cranberries, and apple to flour mixture and stir just until moistened. Divide batter evenly among muffin liners. Sprinkle evenly with streusel.

6 Bake until toothpick inserted into center of muffins comes out clean, about 22 minutes. Cool in pan on wire rack 10 minutes. Remove muffins from pan and cool completely on rack.

7 **SmartPoints value per serving** (1 muffin): 205 Cal, 7 g Total Fat, 1 g Sat Fat, 199 mg Sod, 31 g Total Carb, 13 g Sugar, 2 g Fib, 5 g Prot.

Tip

Coarsely chopping the cranberries in a food processor for the batter gives the muffins a pretty red-flecked appearance and ensures that you get a burst of tart cranberry flavor in every bite.

Fruit orchard oatmeal

Serves 4

2   cups fat-free milk

1   cup water

1½   cups old-fashioned oats

2   tablespoons raisins

¾   teaspoon cinnamon

¼   teaspoon salt

1   pear, peeled, cored, and coarsely shredded

2   tablespoons chopped toasted walnuts

1 Combine milk, water, oats, raisins, cinnamon, and salt in large saucepan. Bring to boil; reduce heat and cook, stirring occasionally, until mixture begins to thicken, about 3 minutes.

2 Stir in pear and cook 2 minutes longer. Spoon oatmeal evenly into 4 bowls; sprinkle evenly with walnuts, serve at once.

6 **SmartPoints value per serving** (¾ cup oatmeal and ½ tablespoon walnuts): 217 Cal, 5 g Total Fat, 1 g Sat Fat, 199 mg Sod, 37 g Total Carb, 14 g Sugar, 5 g Fib, 9 g Prot.

Tip

For a seasonal treat, top the oatmeal with fresh pomegranate arils. Look for them in the refrigerated section of the produce aisle or to prepare them yourself, see the tip on page 175.

Pomegranate-papaya smoothie

Serves 4

2   **cups peeled, seeded, and chopped papaya**

1   **cup frozen whole unsweetened strawberries**

¾   **cup pomegranate juice**

½   **cup vanilla fat-free yogurt**

¼   **cup pomegranate arils**

Place papaya, strawberries, pomegranate juice, and yogurt in blender and puree. Pour into 4 glasses and sprinkle evenly with pomegranate arils.

5 **SmartPoints value per serving** (¾ cup with 1 tablespoon pomegranate arils): 105 Cal, 0 g Total Fat, 0 g Sat Fat, 25 mg Sod, 25 g Total Carb, 17 g Sugar, 2 g Fib, 2 g Prot.

Tip
To juice a pomegranate, pierce a fruit all over with a small sharp knife. Place in a zip-close plastic bag, seal, and roll on a work surface until the crackling stops. Cut a corner of the bag and drain off juice.

Ruby winter vegetable soup

Serves 8

2 teaspoons olive oil

2 red onions, chopped

4 garlic cloves, finely chopped

½ teaspoon ground allspice

4 cups loosely packed thinly sliced red cabbage

1 pound beets, peeled and shredded

1 (32-ounce) carton reduced-sodium chicken broth

2 cups water

2 carrots, cut into ½-inch pieces

2 parsnips, peeled and cut into ½-inch pieces

1 bay leaf

¾ teaspoon salt

½ teaspoon black pepper

1 (14½-ounce) can diced tomatoes

3 tablespoons chopped fresh dill plus additional for garnish

2 tablespoons balsamic vinegar

1 Heat oil in large Dutch oven over medium heat. Add onion and cook, stirring occasionally, until softened, 5 minutes. Add garlic and allspice and cook, stirring constantly, until fragrant, 30 seconds.

2 Stir in cabbage and beets and cook, covered, stirring occasionally, until vegetables are softened, 8 minutes. Stir in broth, water, carrots, parsnips, bay leaf, salt, and pepper and bring to boil. Reduce heat and cook, covered, until vegetables are tender, about 15 minutes. Stir in tomatoes and cook, covered, 10 minutes.

3 Remove and discard bay leaf. Stir in dill and vinegar. Ladle soup evenly into 8 soup bowls and sprinkle with fresh dill.

2 **SmartPoints value per serving** (about 1⅓ cups): 113 Cal, 2 g Total Fat, 0 g Sat Fat, 623 mg Sod, 24 g Total Carb, 12 g Sugar, 6 g Fib, 4 g Prot.

Tip
To make a pretty presentation if you're serving the soup for company, swirl the top of each serving with ZeroPoint™ plain fat-free yogurt.

Carrot-parsnip soup

Carrot-parsnip soup

Serves 4

1	tablespoon unsalted butter
1	large leek, halved lengthwise and sliced, white and light green parts only
2	garlic cloves, finely chopped
2	teaspoons minced peeled fresh ginger
1	pound carrots, cut into ½-inch pieces
1	pound parsnips, peeled and cut into ½-inch pieces
1	(32-ounce) carton reduced-sodium vegetable broth
2	star anises
1	teaspoon salt
¼	teaspoon black pepper
½	cup fat-free half-and-half
2	tablespoons chopped fresh flat-leaf parsley

1 Melt butter in large saucepan over medium heat. Add leek and cook, covered, stirring occasionally, until softened, about 4 minutes. Add garlic and ginger and cook, stirring constantly, just until fragrant, 30 seconds.

2 Stir in carrots, parsnips, broth, star anises, salt, and pepper and bring to boil. Reduce heat and simmer, covered, until vegetables are very tender, about 40 minutes. Remove and discard star anises. Stir in half-and-half and let cool 5 minutes. Puree soup in blender in batches.

3 Return soup to saucepan. Cook over medium heat, stirring occasionally, until heated through, about 2 minutes. Ladle soup evenly into 4 soup bowls and sprinkle with parsley.

6 **SmartPoints value per serving** (1¾ cups): 206 Cal, 4 g Total Fat, 2 g Sat Fat, 908 mg Sod, 41 g Total Carb, 15 g Sugar, 9 g Fib, 4 g Prot.

Tip
Fragrant star anise has a distinctive licorice flavor that infuses the soup as it simmers. If you can't find it, you can substitute ¾ teaspoon five-spice powder or cinnamon in this recipe.

Kale salad with sweet potato and coconut

Serves 6

1	**pound sweet potatoes, peeled and cut into 1-inch pieces**
¾	**teaspoon salt**
½	**teaspoon curry powder**
¼	**teaspoon black pepper**
2	**tablespoons lime juice**
4	**teaspoons canola oil**
½	**small jalapeño pepper, seeded and finely chopped**
1	**small garlic clove, minced**
½	**teaspoon grated peeled fresh ginger**
4	**cups loosely packed torn kale**
⅓	**cup thinly sliced red onion**
⅓	**cup unsweetened coconut chips, toasted**

1 Preheat oven to 425°F. Spray large rimmed baking sheet with nonstick spray.

2 Place sweet potatoes on baking sheet. Sprinkle with ¼ teaspoon salt, curry powder, and black pepper. Lightly spray potatoes with nonstick spray and toss to coat; spread to form even layer. Roast, stirring once, until fork-tender and browned, 20–25 minutes. Let cool.

3 Meanwhile, to make dressing, whisk together lime juice, oil, jalapeño, garlic, ginger, and remaining ½ teaspoon of salt in large bowl.

4 Add sweet potatoes, kale, onion, and coconut chips to dressing and toss to coat. Serve at once.

5 **SmartPoints value per serving** (about 1 cup): 146 Cal, 7 g Total Fat, 4 g Sat Fat, 340 mg Sod, 19 g Total Carb, 4 g Sugar, 4 g Fib, 2 g Prot.

Tip
Coconut chips are a snack food made from large strips of coconut that are baked until crispy. Some chips come already toasted, but if yours are not, you can toast them by cooking and stirring in a skillet over medium heat for 4 minutes.

Kale salad with
sweet potato
and coconut

Asian spaghetti squash salad

Serves 8

1 **(2½-pound) spaghetti squash, halved lengthwise and seeded**

2 **tablespoons rice vinegar**

1 **teaspoon minced peeled fresh ginger**

½ **teaspoon Asian (dark) sesame oil**

½ **teaspoon salt**

⅛ **teaspoon red pepper flakes**

1 **red bell pepper, diced**

½ **English (seedless) cucumber, cut into matchstick strips**

1 **serrano or jalapeño pepper, seeded and minced**

1 **large scallion, thinly sliced**

¼ **cup chopped fresh cilantro**

1 Place squash halves cut side down in microwavable dish. Cover with wax paper and microwave on High until tender when pierced with knife, 18–20 minutes. Turn squash over and let cool 5 minutes. With fork, scrape squash into large bowl and let cool completely.

2 Meanwhile, to make dressing, whisk together vinegar, ginger, sesame oil, salt, and red pepper flakes in small bowl.

3 Add bell pepper, cucumber, and serrano to squash and toss to combine. Add dressing and toss gently to coat.

4 Serve at room temperature, or transfer to airtight container and refrigerate until chilled, at least 2 hours. Sprinkle with scallion and cilantro just before serving.

0 **SmartPoints value per serving** (generous ½ cup): 54 Cal, 1 g Total Fat, 0 g Sat Fat, 171 mg Sod, 11 g Total Carb, 1 g Sugar, 1 g Fib, 1 g Prot.

Wheat berry-apple salad

Serves 8

1   cup wheat berries

2   tablespoons white wine vinegar

2   tablespoons unsweetened
     apple juice

1   tablespoon olive oil

1   tablespoon minced peeled
     fresh ginger

½   teaspoon salt

2   Gala apples, cored and diced

2   celery stalks, thinly sliced

1   small red onion, diced

½   cup raisins

¼   cup sliced almonds, toasted

¼   cup chopped fresh flat-leaf
     parsley

1 Bring large pot of water to boil over medium-high heat; stir in wheat berries. Reduce heat and simmer, covered, until berries are tender but still chewy, 45 minutes–1 hour. Drain in colander and rinse under cold running water; drain again.

2 Whisk together vinegar, apple juice, oil, ginger, and salt in large bowl. Add wheat berries, apples, celery, onion, raisins, almonds, and parsley and toss to combine.

5 **SmartPoints value per serving** (about ¾ cup): 174 Cal, 4 g Total Fat, 0 g Sat Fat, 157 mg Sod, 33 g Total Carb, 13 g Sugar, 5 g Fib, 5 g Prot.

Spicy turkey, apple,
and spinach panini

Spicy turkey, apple, and spinach panini

Serves 4

2 tablespoons reduced-fat chipotle mayonnaise

4 (1½-ounce) slices multigrain bread

16 very thin apple slices

6 ounces thinly sliced skinless deli smoked turkey breast

1 cup loosely packed baby spinach

2 (1-ounce) slices reduced-fat Cheddar

1 Spread ½ tablespoon mayonnaise on one side of each bread slice. Top 2 bread slices evenly with apple slices, turkey, spinach, and Cheddar. Top with remaining 2 bread slices mayonnaise side down. Lightly spray sandwiches with olive oil nonstick spray.

2 Spray large ridged grill pan with olive oil nonstick spray and set over medium-high heat. Place sandwiches in pan and top with another heavy skillet to weight them. Cook until cheese is melted and bread is golden brown and crispy, 2–3 minutes on each side (or grill sandwich in panini press). Cut each sandwich in half.

6 **SmartPoints value per serving** (½ sandwich): 253 Cal, 8 g Total Fat, 3 g Sat Fat, 536 mg Sod, 27 g Total Carb, 8 g Sugar, 4 g Fib, 18 g Prot.

Tip
To add more spice to the sandwiches, use peppery baby arugula or watercress instead of spinach. You can also add a few sprigs of fresh cilantro to each sandwich for a pungent kick.

Grilled chicken, broccoli rabe, and Peppadew sandwiches

Serves 4

½   **pound broccoli rabe, trimmed and coarsely chopped (about ½ bunch)**

2   **(5-ounce) skinless boneless chicken breasts**

½   **teaspoon salt**

⅛   **teaspoon black pepper**

2   **teaspoons olive oil**

1   **garlic clove, finely chopped**

⅛   **teaspoon red pepper flakes**

1   **(12-inch) loaf ciabatta, split (about 9 ounces)**

4   **ounces reduced-fat provolone, shredded**

2   **tablespoons chopped Peppadew peppers**

1 Bring large saucepan of lightly salted water to boil. Add broccoli rabe and cook, covered, until tender, about 4 minutes. Drain.

2 Meanwhile, sprinkle chicken with ¼ teaspoon of salt and pepper. Heat 1 teaspoon of oil in medium skillet over medium-high heat. Add chicken and cook until browned and cooked through, 5–6 minutes per side. Transfer to cutting board and thinly slice.

3 Add remaining 1 teaspoon of oil to same skillet. Reduce heat to medium. Add garlic and red pepper flakes and cook, stirring constantly, just until fragrant, 30 seconds. Add broccoli rabe and remaining ¼ teaspoon of salt and cook, stirring constantly, about 1 minute.

4 Remove soft center from ciabatta and discard (or save for bread crumbs). Place half of provolone on bottom of bread. Top with chicken, broccoli rabe, Peppadew peppers, remaining cheese, and top of loaf.

5 Spray large ridged grill pan with olive oil nonstick spray and set over medium-high heat. Place sandwich in pan and top with another heavy skillet to weight it. Cook until cheese is melted and bread is golden brown and crispy, 2–3 minutes on each side (or grill sandwich in panini press). Cut crosswise into 4 pieces.

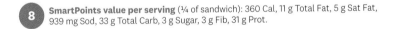

(8)   **SmartPoints value per serving** (¼ of sandwich): 360 Cal, 11 g Total Fat, 5 g Sat Fat, 939 mg Sod, 33 g Total Carb, 3 g Sugar, 3 g Fib, 31 g Prot.

Tip
Peppadews are sweet-hot peppers that look like a cross between a mini–red bell pepper and a cherry tomato. Look for jars of them in the deli section of supermarkets, or use pepperoncini.

Roasted Brussels sprouts with cranberries and walnuts

Serves 4

1¼ **pounds fresh Brussels sprouts, trimmed and halved**

2   **teaspoons olive oil**

¾   **teaspoon salt**

¼   **teaspoon black pepper**

¼   **cup orange juice**

3   **tablespoons dried cranberries, coarsely chopped**

¼   **teaspoon grated orange zest**

2   **tablespoons walnuts, toasted and coarsely chopped**

1 Preheat oven to 450°F. Spray large rimmed baking sheet with nonstick spray.

2 Place Brussels sprouts in prepared pan; drizzle with oil. Sprinkle with salt and pepper. Toss sprouts until coated evenly and spread to form even layer. Roast sprouts, stirring once, until tender and browned, 15–20 minutes.

3 Meanwhile, place orange juice in microwavable cup and microwave on High until hot, about 10 seconds. Add cranberries and let stand.

4 Transfer sprouts to medium bowl and stir in cranberry mixture and orange zest. Sprinkle Brussels sprouts with walnuts and serve.

3 **SmartPoints value per serving** (¾ cup): 130 Cal, 5 g Total Fat, 1 g Sat Fat, 472 mg Sod, 19 g Total Carb, 9 g Sugar, 6 g Fib, 5 g Prot.

Tip

Roasting Brussels sprouts brings out their sweetness and gives them an appealing caramelized color. Try this recipe to convert any Brussels sprouts-haters in your family.

Butternut squash with hoisin

Serves 6

2	teaspoons canola oil
1	shallot, finely chopped
2	teaspoons finely chopped peeled fresh ginger
1	medium (about 1¾-pounds) butternut squash, peeled, seeded, and cut in 1-inch chunks (3¾ cups)
¾	cup water
1	tablespoon rice wine or dry sherry
2	teaspoons reduced-sodium soy sauce
¼	teaspoon salt
2	tablespoons hoisin sauce
¼	teaspoon hot chili oil
2	thin scallions, thinly sliced
2	tablespoons chopped fresh cilantro

1 Heat wok or large deep skillet over high heat until drop of water sizzles in pan. Add canola oil and swirl to coat wok. Add shallot and ginger and stir-fry until fragrant, 30 seconds.

2 Add squash and stir-fry 1 minute. Add water, wine, soy sauce, and salt. Reduce heat and cook, covered, stirring occasionally, just until squash is tender, about 10 minutes. Stir in hoisin sauce and hot chili oil and cook 1 minute. Sprinkle with scallions and cilantro.

1 **SmartPoints value per serving** (½ cup): 95 Cal, 2 g Total Fat, 0 g Sat Fat, 247 mg Sod, 19 g Total Carb, 5 g Sugar, 3 g Fib, 2 g Prot.

Tip
If you don't have hot chili oil, add ¼ teaspoon red pepper flakes along with the shallot and ginger in step 1.

Moroccan chicken with oranges

Serves 4

½   **teaspoon smoked paprika**
½   **teaspoon ground cumin**
¼   **teaspoon ground turmeric**
½   **teaspoon salt**
¼   **teaspoon black pepper**
2   **teaspoons olive oil**
4   **(5-ounce) thin-sliced skinless boneless chicken cutlets**
2   **large navel oranges**
1   **tablespoon water**
1½ **teaspoons honey**
Minced fresh mint

1 Stir together paprika, cumin, turmeric, salt, and pepper in small cup.

2 Heat 1 teaspoon of oil in large nonstick skillet over medium heat. Sprinkle chicken with half of spice mixture. Add chicken to skillet and cook, turning once, until chicken is cooked through, about 6 minutes. Transfer chicken to plate.

3 Meanwhile grate 1 teaspoon of zest from one orange and set aside. With sharp knife, cut off slice from top and bottom of oranges. Stand fruit upright. Cut off peel and white pith, cutting from top to bottom, turning fruit as you go. Cut oranges crosswise into rounds about ⅜ inch thick; cut rounds in half.

4 Add remaining 1 teaspoon oil to skillet. Add orange slices, orange zest, the water, remaining spice mixture, and honey to skillet and cook, stirring constantly, just until heated through, about 1 minute. Spoon orange mixture over chicken. Sprinkle with mint.

1 **SmartPoints value per serving** (1 chicken cutlet and about ¼ cup orange mixture): 242 Cal, 6 g Total Fat, 1 g Sat Fat, 354 mg Sod, 14 g Total Carb, 11 g Sugar, 3 g Fib, 33 g Prot.

Roasted whole chicken with apples and sausage

Serves 8

2   **(5-ounce) links Italian turkey sausage**

¼   **cup chopped fresh flat-leaf parsley**

1   **tablespoon fresh thyme leaves, chopped**

2   **garlic cloves, minced**

1   **teaspoon salt**

¾   **teaspoon black pepper**

1   **(3¼-pound) whole chicken**

4   **apples, quartered**

1   **large red onion, cut through root end into 8 wedges**

1½   **cups apple cider**

1 Preheat oven to 425°F. Spray large roasting pan with nonstick spray.

2 Prick sausage all over with fork and transfer to medium skillet. Add enough cold water to cover and bring to boil. Reduce heat and simmer until sausage is firm, about 5 minutes. Drain, cool slightly, and cut into ½-inch slices.

3 Combine parsley, thyme, garlic, ¾ teaspoon of salt, and ½ teaspoon of pepper in small bowl. Place chicken breast side down on cutting board. Using kitchen shears or knife, cut through ribs on each side of backbone and discard. Turn chicken over and use your hands to flatten chicken. Gently lift skin from chicken and spread herb mixture evenly under skin. Place chicken in center of prepared pan. Tuck wing tips under chicken.

4 Scatter apples, onion, and sausage around chicken. Sprinkle apple mixture with remaining ¼ teaspoon salt and remaining ¼ teaspoon pepper; lightly spray with nonstick spray. Roast until instant-read thermometer inserted into chicken thigh (not touching bone) registers 165°F, 50–55 minutes, stirring apple mixture once halfway through roasting time.

5 Transfer chicken and apple mixture to platter and cover to keep warm. Strain pan juices into measuring cup. Add cider to roasting pan and set over 2 burners. Bring to boil over high heat, scraping browned bits from bottom of pan. Cook, stirring occasionally, until cider is reduced by half, about 6 minutes. Strain cider mixture into measuring cup and skim off visible fat. Carve chicken into 8 pieces and serve with apple mixture and sauce. Remove skin before eating chicken.

 SmartPoints value per serving (1 piece chicken with ½ cup apple mixture and about 2 tablespoons sauce): 236 Cal, 6 g Total Fat, 1 g Sat Fat, 580 mg Sod, 21 g Total Carb, 15 g Sugar, 3 g Fib, 26 g Prot.

Tip
Look for local apple cider, which is simply unfiltered apple juice, at farmers' markets. The flavor of cider will vary from farm to farm or even week to week depending on the types of apples used.

Roasted whole chicken
with apples and sausage

Chicken and vegetables
with balsamic-espresso glaze

Chicken and vegetables with balsamic-espresso glaze

Serves 6

1½ pounds rutabaga, peeled and cut into 1-inch pieces

4 large carrots, cut in half lengthwise and cut into 2-inch pieces

1 large onion, cut into wedges

2 teaspoons olive oil

3 teaspoons chopped fresh rosemary

¾ teaspoon salt

½ teaspoon black pepper

6 (5-ounce) skinless bone-in chicken thighs, trimmed

⅓ cup balsamic vinegar

3 tablespoons packed dark brown sugar

1½ teaspoons instant espresso powder

1 Preheat oven to 425°F. Spray large roasting pan with olive oil nonstick spray.

2 Combine rutabaga, carrots, and onion in prepared pan and drizzle with oil. Sprinkle with 2 teaspoons of rosemary, ¼ teaspoon of salt, and ¼ teaspoon of pepper. Toss to coat and spread vegetables evenly to edge of pan. Sprinkle chicken with remaining ½ teaspoon of salt and remaining ¼ teaspoon of pepper and place in center of pan. Roast 20 minutes.

3 Meanwhile, to make glaze, stir together vinegar, brown sugar, espresso powder, and remaining 1 teaspoon of rosemary in small saucepan. Bring to boil. Reduce heat and simmer until thickened and slightly syrupy, about 4 minutes (you should have ¼ cup).

4 Stir vegetables and brush chicken with 2 tablespoons glaze; roast 10 minutes. Brush chicken with remaining 2 tablespoons glaze and roast until vegetables are tender and instant-read thermometer inserted into centers of thighs registers 165°F, about 10 minutes longer. Serve chicken with vegetables.

6 **SmartPoints value per serving** (1 chicken thigh with about ⅔ cup vegetables): 298 Cal, 8 g Total Fat, 2 g Sat Fat, 477 mg Sod, 26 g Total Carb, 17 g Sugar, 4 g Fib, 30 g Prot.

Tip
With light tan bottoms and violet tops, rutabagas look like large turnips. They taste similar, too, having a delicately sweet yet slightly bitter flavor that mellows with cooking.

Lemon-rosemary chicken with radicchio

Serves 4

Grated zest of 1 lemon
2 garlic cloves, minced
2 teaspoons finely chopped fresh rosemary
¼ teaspoon salt
½ teaspoon black pepper
4 (6- to 7-ounce) bone-in skin-on chicken thighs
1 tablespoon balsamic vinegar
2 teaspoons extra-virgin olive oil
1 large head radicchio (about 10 ounces), cut into 4 wedges

1 Preheat oven to 425°F.

2 Stir together lemon zest, garlic, rosemary, ½ teaspoon of salt, and ¼ teaspoon of pepper in cup. Spread evenly onto chicken under skin of each thigh. Spray large heavy ovenproof skillet with nonstick spray and set over medium-high heat. Add chicken skin-side down and cook until golden, about 5 minutes.

3 Meanwhile, whisk together vinegar, oil, remaining ¼ teaspoon of salt, and ¼ teaspoon of pepper in large bowl. Add radicchio and toss to coat.

4 Transfer chicken to plate and drain off and discard fat from pan. Return chicken to skillet and add radicchio cut sides up. Transfer skillet to oven and roast until radicchio is tender and instant-read thermometer inserted into thighs registers 165°F, about 20 minutes. With tongs, transfer chicken and radicchio to platter; drizzle top with pan juices. Remove skin before eating chicken.

4 **SmartPoints value per serving** (1 chicken thigh with 1 wedge radicchio and about 2 teaspoons pan juices): 213 Cal, 8 g Total Fat, 2 g Sat Fat, 587 mg Sod, 5 g Total Carb, 1 g Sugar, 1 g Fib, 29 g Prot.

Tip
Radicchio looks like a small loose-leafed red cabbage. It has a crunchy texture and somewhat bitter flavor and is commonly used in salads. In this roasted version, it develops a complex sweet flavor.

Slow-cooker Middle Eastern beef stew

Serves 6

1   **tablespoon all-purpose flour**

1½ **teaspoon salt**

½   **plus ⅛ teaspoon ground allspice**

¼   **teaspoon black pepper**

1   **pound boneless lean beef bottom round, trimmed and cut into 2-inch chunks**

3   **teaspoons olive oil**

2   **onions, chopped**

4   **garlic cloves, minced**

½   **cup dry red wine**

1   **cup reduced-sodium beef broth**

1   **pound sweet potatoes, peeled and cut into 2-inch pieces**

½   **pound carrots, cut into 2-inch pieces**

1   **tablespoon pomegranate molasses**

2   **cups cooked whole wheat couscous**

Thinly sliced fresh mint

1 Stir together flour, ½ teaspoon of salt, ½ teaspoon of allspice, and pepper in medium bowl. Add beef and toss to coat.

2 Heat 1½ teaspoons of oil in large heavy skillet over medium-high heat. Add beef, in batches and cook, stirring occasionally, until browned on all sides, about 6 minutes. Transfer beef to 5- or 6-quart slow cooker.

3 Add remaining 1½ teaspoons oil to same skillet. Add onions; reduce heat and cook, covered, stirring occasionally, until softened, 5 minutes. Add garlic and cook, stirring constantly, until fragrant, 30 seconds. Add wine and bring to boil, scraping up browned bits from bottom of skillet. Transfer to slow cooker and stir in broth, sweet potatoes, carrots, and ½ teaspoon of salt. Cover and cook until beef and vegetables are tender, 4–5 hours on High or 7–8 hours on Low.

4 Stir in molasses, remaining ½ teaspoon salt, and remaining ⅛ teaspoon allspice. Serve over couscous. Sprinkle with mint.

8   **SmartPoints value per serving** (1 cup stew and ⅓ cup couscous): 325 Cal, 7 g Total Fat, 2 g Sat Fat, 761 mg Sod, 43 g Total Carb, 10 g Sugar, 7 g Fib, 22 g Prot.

Tip
Pomegranate molasses is an important ingredient in Middle Eastern cuisine (it's also fabulous in marinades and barbecue sauce). If it is unavailable, substitute 1½ teaspoons balsamic vinegar and ½ teaspoon honey in this recipe.

Rosemary steak with apple-horseradish relish

Serves 4

1½ teaspoons chopped fresh
 rosemary

¾ teaspoon salt

¼ teaspoon black pepper

1 (1-pound) lean flank steak,
 trimmed

1 tablespoon prepared
 horseradish, drained

2 tablespoons lemon juice

2 tablespoons chopped fresh
 flat-leaf parsley

1 tablespoon minced red onion

1½ teaspoons honey

2 apples, cored and cut into
 ¼-inch pieces

1 Stir together rosemary, ¼ teaspoon of salt, and pepper in cup. Rub herb mixture on both sides of steak and lightly spray with nonstick spray.

2 Heat large ridged grill pan over medium-high heat. Add steak to pan and cook, turning occasionally, until instant-read thermometer inserted into side of steak registers 145°F, about 10 minutes. Transfer steak to cutting board and let stand 5 minutes.

3 Meanwhile, to make relish, stir together horseradish, lemon juice, parsley, onion, honey, and remaining ½ teaspoon of salt in medium bowl; stir in apples. Cut steak on diagonal into 16 thin slices. Serve with relish.

4 **SmartPoints value per serving** (4 slices steak with ½ cup relish): 234 Cal, 8 g Total Fat, 2 g Sat Fat, 528 mg Sod, 17 g Total Carb, 13 g Sugar, 2 g Fib, 25 g Prot.

Tip
Depending on your preference, use a tart apple like Granny Smith or a sweet one like Golden Delicious to make the relish. A combination of apple varieties is OK to use, too.

Rosemary steak with apple-horseradish relish

Pork chops with
apples and ginger

Pork chops with apples and ginger

Serves 4

1	**teaspoon ground coriander**
¾	**teaspoon salt**
½	**teaspoon ground cumin**
¼	**teaspoon black pepper**
2	**teaspoons olive oil**
4	**(5-ounce) lean center-cut boneless pork loin chops, trimmed**
1	**large shallot, finely chopped**
1	**tablespoon grated peeled fresh ginger**
2	**apples, cored and cut into ½-inch pieces**
⅓	**cup chicken broth**
2	**tablespoons whole-grain mustard**
2	**tablespoons chopped fresh flat-leaf parsley**

1 Stir together ¼ teaspoon of coriander, ½ teaspoon of salt, ¼ teaspoon of cumin, and pepper in cup. Rub spice mixture onto both sides of pork.

2 Heat oil in large heavy skillet over medium-high heat. Add pork and cook, turning once, until instant-read thermometer inserted into sides of chops registers 145°F, 5–6 minutes. Transfer to plate.

3 Spray same skillet with olive oil nonstick spray. Add shallot and ginger; reduce heat and cook, stirring constantly, until shallot softens, 1–2 minutes. Add apples and remaining ¾ teaspoon coriander, remaining ¼ teaspoon of salt, and remaining ¼ teaspoon of cumin. Cook, stirring occasionally, until apples begin to soften, about 2 minutes. Stir in broth and scrape up browned bits from bottom of pan. Cover and cook until apples are tender, about 3 minutes. Return pork and any accumulated juices to skillet and cook until heated through, 1–2 minutes. Stir in mustard. Sprinkle with parsley and serve.

5 **SmartPoints value per serving** (1 pork chop with ½ cup apple mixture): 286 Cal, 11 g Total Fat, 3 g Sat Fat, 665 mg Sod, 16 g Total Carb, 11 g Sugar, 3 g Fib, 31 g Prot.

Tip

Serve the pork chops with heat-and-serve brown rice available in plastic pouches near the dry rice in supermarkets (⅓ cup cooked brown rice will increase the per-serving SmartPoints by 2).

Cajun shrimp with garlicky spinach grits

Serves 4

4	**teaspoons olive oil**
2	**large garlic cloves, minced**
1	**(14½-ounce) can reduced-sodium chicken broth**
¼	**cup water**
½	**teaspoon salt**
½	**cup quick-cooking grits**
3	**cups firmly packed baby spinach**
1¼	**teaspoons Cajun or Creole seasoning**
1	**pound medium peeled and deveined shrimp**

1 Heat 2 teaspoons of oil in large saucepan over medium heat. Add garlic and cook, stirring constantly, just until fragrant, 30 seconds. Add broth, water, and ¼ teaspoon of salt and bring to boil. Gradually stir in grits. Reduce heat and cook, covered, stirring occasionally, until grits thicken, about 5 minutes.

2 Remove saucepan from heat and stir in spinach in batches until wilted. Cover and keep warm.

3 Meanwhile, stir together remaining 2 teaspoons of oil, Cajun seasoning, and remaining ½ teaspoon salt in medium bowl. Add shrimp and toss to coat. Set large ridged grill pan over medium-high heat until hot. Add half of shrimp to pan and cook, turning once, until just opaque in center, 3–4 minutes. Transfer to plate. Repeat with remaining shrimp.

4 Divide grits mixture among 4 shallow bowls and top evenly with shrimp.

5 **SmartPoints value per serving** (½ cup grits mixture with about 8 shrimp): 207 Cal, 6 g Total Fat, 1 g Sat Fat, 1,417 mg Sod, 19 g Total Carb, 1 g Sugar, 1 g Fib, 25 g Prot.

Cajun shrimp with
garlicky spinach grits

Grilled tuna with blood orange salsa

Serves 4

3   blood oranges or navel oranges, peeled, sectioned, and cut into ½-inch pieces

½   small fennel bulb, diced

4   green olives, pitted and finely chopped

2   tablespoons chopped fresh flat-leaf parsley

2   teaspoons extra-virgin olive oil

¾   teaspoon salt

¼   teaspoon black pepper

4   (5-ounce) tuna steaks

1 To make salsa, stir together oranges, fennel, olives, parsley, oil, ¼ teaspoon of salt, and ⅛ teaspoon of pepper in medium bowl.

2 Sprinkle tuna with remaining ½ teaspoon of salt and remaining ⅛ teaspoon of pepper. Spray large ridged grill pan with olive oil nonstick spray and set over medium-high heat until hot. Add tuna to pan and cook, turning once, just until pink in center, 4–6 minutes. Serve tuna with salsa.

1 **SmartPoints value per serving** (1 tuna steak with ⅓ cup salsa): 254 Cal, 4 g Total Fat, 1 g Sat Fat, 543 mg Sod, 19 g Total Carb, 14 g Sugar, 4 g Fib, 36 g Prot.

Tip
Blood oranges have pink-tinged orange skin and ruby red flesh. They are usually a little smaller than a regular orange, and the flavor is more tart—like a cross between an orange and a pink grapefruit.

African-style vegetable curry

Serves 4

1	**(14-ounce) container extra-firm tofu**
½	**teaspoon salt**
¼	**teaspoon black pepper**
1	**teaspoon canola oil**
1	**onion, chopped**
2	**garlic cloves, finely chopped**
½	**jalapeño pepper, seeded and finely chopped**
1½	**teaspoons curry powder**
1	**teaspoon grated peeled fresh ginger**
1½	**cups reduced-sodium vegetable broth**
1	**(14½-ounce) can diced tomatoes**
1	**tablespoon peanut butter**
½	**pound mustard greens, trimmed and coarsely chopped**
2	**tablespoons chopped unsalted dry roasted peanuts**

1 Place tofu between 2 flat plates. Weight top plate with heavy can or cast-iron skillet until tofu bulges at sides but does not split. Let stand about 30 minutes; pour off excess liquid.

2 Preheat oven to 425°F. Spray large rimmed baking sheet with nonstick spray.

3 Cut tofu into ½-inch cubes; spread to form single layer in prepared pan. Sprinkle tofu with ¼ teaspoon of salt and pepper and lightly spray with nonstick spray. Roast tofu until golden, stirring once, 20–25 minutes.

4 Meanwhile, heat oil in large heavy skillet over medium-high heat. Add onion and cook, covered, stirring occasionally, until softened, 5 minutes. Add garlic, jalapeño, curry powder, and ginger and cook, stirring constantly, just until fragrant, 30 seconds. Stir in broth, tomatoes, peanut butter, and remaining ¼ teaspoon of salt and bring to boil. Stir in mustard greens in batches and return to boil. Reduce heat and cook, covered, until greens are tender, 5 minutes. Stir in tofu and cook until heated through, 1 minute. Spoon into 4 dishes and sprinkle with peanuts.

2 **SmartPoints value per serving** (1¼ cups): 212 Cal, 11 g Total Fat, 2 g Sat Fat, 546 mg Sod, 17 g Total Carb, 6 g Sugar, 6 g Fib, 16 g Prot.

Tip
For an extra 2 SmartPoints value, accompany each serving of vegetable curry with ⅓ cup cooked brown rice.

Penne with
roasted cauliflower
and feta

Penne with roasted cauliflower and feta

Serves 4

2   **(12-ounce) bags fresh cauliflower florets, cut into 1½-inch pieces**

1   **red onion, sliced**

¾   **teaspoon salt**

¼   **teaspoon black pepper**

2   **garlic cloves, minced**

2   **teaspoons minced fresh oregano, plus additional for garnish**

6   **ounces whole wheat penne**

½   **cup crumbled reduced-fat feta cheese**

1   **teaspoon extra-virgin olive oil**

Chopped fresh mint, for garnish (optional)

1 Preheat oven to 450°F. Spray large rimmed baking sheet with nonstick spray.

2 Place cauliflower and onion in prepared pan. Sprinkle with ¼ teaspoon salt and the pepper and lightly spray with olive oil nonstick spray. Toss to coat and spread vegetables in single layer. Roast until crisp-tender, about 15 minutes. Stir in garlic and 2 teaspoons oregano. Spray again with olive oil nonstick spray and roast until vegetables are tender, about 5 minutes longer.

3 Meanwhile, cook pasta according to package directions. Drain, reserving ½ cup cooking water.

4 Return pasta to same pot. Stir in cauliflower mixture, feta, oil, remaining ½ teaspoon salt, and enough reserved cooking water to evenly moisten pasta and vegetables. Divide among 4 plates and sprinkle with additional oregano and fresh mint if using.

5 **SmartPoints value per serving** (2 cups): 247 Cal, 5 g Total Fat, 2 g Sat Fat, 679 mg Sod, 44 g Total Carb, 6 g Sugar, 8 g Fib, 12 g Prot.

Tip
If you use a head of cauliflower and cut your own florets, you will need about 6 cups of florets for this recipe.

Broccoli and Cheddar mac and cheese

Serves 6

1½ **cups whole wheat macaroni**

4 **cups small fresh broccoli florets**

2 **tablespoons olive oil**

1 **garlic clove, minced**

2 **tablespoons all-purpose flour**

2 **cups low-fat (1%) milk**

¼ **pound extra-sharp Cheddar cheese, shredded (1 cup)**

¼ **cup plus 1 tablespoon grated Parmesan**

1 **teaspoon Dijon mustard**

1 **teaspoon salt**

⅛ **teaspoon cayenne**

¼ **cup whole wheat panko bread crumbs**

1 Spray 2-quart flameproof baking pan with nonstick spray.

2 Cook macaroni according to package directions, adding broccoli during last 2 minutes of cooking time. Drain well.

3 Meanwhile, to make sauce, heat oil in large saucepan over medium heat. Add garlic and cook, stirring constantly, until fragrant, 30 seconds. Add flour and cook, whisking constantly, 1 minute. Gradually whisk in milk. Cook, whisking often, until mixture comes to boil and thickens, about 8 minutes. Remove from heat and add Cheddar, ¼ cup Parmesan, mustard, salt, and cayenne. Stir until cheese melts.

4 Preheat broiler.

5 Add broccoli and macaroni to sauce. Stir to combine and pour into prepared baking pan. Stir together panko and remaining 1 tablespoon Parmesan in small bowl; sprinkle evenly over pasta. Lightly spray topping with nonstick spray. Broil 6 inches from heat until crumbs are lightly browned, about 3 minutes.

10 **SmartPoints value per serving** (1 cup): 313 Cal, 14 g Total Fat, 6 g Sat Fat, 693 mg Sod, 35 g Total Carb, 5 g Sugar, 4 g Fib, 15 g Prot.

Parsnip-pear mini cupcakes with cream cheese frosting

Makes 12

Cupcakes

⅔   **cup all-purpose flour**

1   **teaspoon cinnamon**

½   **teaspoon baking powder**

¼   **teaspoon baking soda**

¼   **teaspoon salt**

Pinch ground nutmeg

1   **large egg**

3   **tablespoons plain low-fat yogurt**

2   **tablespoons canola oil**

½   **teaspoon vanilla extract**

½   **teaspoon grated lemon zest**

⅓   **cup shredded peeled parsnip**

⅓   **cup shredded peeled pear**

Frosting

¼   **cup light cream cheese (Neufchâtel), softened**

2   **tablespoons confectioners' sugar**

1   **teaspoon low-fat (1%) milk**

2   **tablespoons sweetened flaked coconut, toasted**

1 Preheat oven to 350°F.

2 Spray 12-cup mini-muffin pan with cooking spray or line with paper liners.

3 Stir together flour, cinnamon, baking powder, baking soda, salt, and nutmeg in medium bowl. Whisk together egg, yogurt, oil, vanilla, and lemon zest in another medium bowl. Stir parsnip and pear into egg mixture. Add egg mixture to flour mixture and stir just until blended.

4 Fill muffin cups evenly with batter. Bake until toothpick inserted into centers of cupcakes comes out clean, 10–12 minutes. Cool in pan on wire rack 5 minutes. Remove cupcakes from pan and cool completely on rack.

5 To make frosting, with electric mixer on medium speed, beat cream cheese, confectioners' sugar, and milk in medium bowl until smooth. Spread frosting evenly onto cooled cupcakes. Sprinkle with coconut.

 3   **SmartPoints value per serving** (1 mini cupcake): 83 Cal, 4 g Total Fat, 1 g Sat Fat, 123 mg Sod, 9 g Total Carb, 3 g Sugar, 1 g Fib, 2 g Prot.

Gingery winter squash custards with gingersnap crumble

Serves 6

4   **gingersnap cookies, crumbled**

1½   **teaspoons unsalted butter, melted**

⅛   **teaspoon salt**

6   **ounces light cream cheese (Neufchâtel), softened**

3   **tablespoons packed dark brown sugar**

1   **large egg**

¾   **cup cooked mashed winter squash, such as butternut, calabaza, or buttercup**

1   **teaspoon cinnamon**

¼   **teaspoon ground ginger**

6   **tablespoons thawed frozen fat-free whipped topping**

1 Preheat oven to 350°F.

2 Place cookies in zip-close plastic bag and use rolling pin or bottom of small saucepan to crush into coarse crumbs. Transfer to small bowl. Add butter and salt and stir to combine. Place crumbs on small baking sheet and bake, stirring once, until fragrant and lightly browned, about 8–10 minutes. Transfer to plate to cool. Maintain oven temperature.

3 Spray 6 (4-ounce) ramekins with nonstick spray.

4 With hand-held mixer on medium speed, beat cream cheese and brown sugar until fluffy. Add egg and beat until well combined. Beat in squash, cinnamon, and ginger until smooth. Spoon evenly into ramekins. Place ramekins in 9 x 13-inch baking pan and pour in enough hot water to come halfway up sides of ramekins. Bake until set, about 30 minutes.

5 Carefully remove ramekins from baking pan and cool on wire rack. Let stand to cool completely. Cover and refrigerate until chilled, at least 4 hours or up to 2 days. Top each custard with 1 tablespoon whipped topping and sprinkle evenly with gingersnap crumbs just before serving.

6   **SmartPoints value per serving** (1 custard): 158 Cal, 9 g Total Fat, 5 g Sat Fat, 186 mg Sod, 16 g Total Carb, 10 g Sugar, 1 g Fib, 4 g Prot.

Tip
To make ¾ cup of mashed winter squash, simmer 1⅓ cups cubed peeled squash in water until very tender, about 15 minutes. Drain and mash.

Gingery winter squash custards with gingersnap crumble

Carrot-coconut
oatmeal cookies

Carrot-coconut oatmeal cookies

Makes 33

¾   cup whole wheat flour

1½   teaspoons cinnamon

¼   teaspoon baking soda

¼   teaspoon salt

⅛   teaspoon ground ginger

½   cup packed light brown sugar

¼   cup coconut oil, melted and cooled

2   tablespoons plain low-fat yogurt

1   large egg

1   teaspoon vanilla extract

1½   cups old-fashioned oats

1   cup finely shredded carrot

½   cup unsweetened flaked coconut

¼   cup chopped toasted walnuts

¼   cup golden raisins

1 Place oven racks in upper and lower thirds of oven and preheat oven to 350°F. Line 2 large baking sheets with parchment paper.

2 Whisk together flour, cinnamon, baking soda, salt, and ginger in medium bowl. Whisk together brown sugar, oil, yogurt, egg, and vanilla in large bowl. Add flour mixture, oats, carrot, coconut, walnuts, and raisins to brown-sugar mixture and stir to combine.

3 Drop batter by rounded tablespoonfuls 2 inches apart onto prepared baking sheets. Flatten each cookie slightly. Bake until golden brown on bottom, 12–14 minutes, switching and rotating baking sheets halfway through baking time. Cool on baking sheets on wire racks 1 minute. With spatula, transfer cookies to racks and cool completely. Store in airtight container up to 3 days.

3 **SmartPoints value per serving** (1 cookie): 77 Cal, 4 g Total Fat, 2 g Sat Fat, 34 mg Sod, 10 g Total Carb, 4 g Sugar, 1 g Fib, 2 g Prot.

Tip
If the cookies become too soft when you store them, you can toast them in a toaster oven for a couple minutes to re-crisp them.

Citrus olive oil cake

Serves 16

4   **large eggs, separated**
½   **cup granulated sugar**
⅓   **cup extra-virgin olive oil**
⅓   **cup plain low-fat yogurt**
1   **teaspoon grated lemon zest**
1   **tablespoon lemon juice**
1   **teaspoon grated orange zest**
1   **tablespoon orange juice**
½   **teaspoon salt**
1   **cup all-purpose flour**
1   **tablespoon confectioners' sugar**

1 Preheat oven to 350°F. Line 9-inch springform pan with parchment paper and spray with olive oil nonstick spray.

2 With electric mixer on medium speed, beat egg whites and ¼ cup of granulated sugar in medium bowl until soft peaks form when beaters are lifted. Set aside. (Do not wash beaters.)

3 With electric mixer on medium-high speed, beat egg yolks and remaining ¼ cup granulated sugar in another medium bowl until thick and light. With mixer running at medium speed, slowly drizzle in olive oil. Add yogurt, lemon zest and juice, orange zest and juice, and salt and beat to combine. At low speed, add flour and beat just until combined. Gently fold egg-white mixture into batter in three additions until no streaks of white remain.

4 Scrape batter into prepared springform pan and bake until center of cake is set, 45–50 minutes. Cool completely in pan on wire rack.

5 Carefully remove cake from pan. Place confectioners' sugar in small fine wire mesh sieve and sprinkle over cake just before serving.

4   **SmartPoints value per serving** (¹⁄₁₆ of cake): 117 Cal, 6 g Total Fat, 1 g Sat Fat, 92 mg Sod, 13 g Total Carb, 7 g Sugar, 0 g Fib, 3 g Prot.

Tip

For a pretty presentation, serve slices of the cake with segments of pink and white grapefruit alongside.

Citrus olive oil cake

Kumquat and ginger compote

Serves 9

½	**vanilla bean, split in half lengthwise**
⅓	**cup sugar**
⅓	**cup riesling or other sweet white wine**
⅓	**cup water**
2	**whole cloves**
2	**cups kumquats, halved lengthwise and seeded (about ¾ pound)**
3	**tablespoons chopped crystallized ginger**

1 Scrape seeds from vanilla bean into medium saucepan. Add vanilla bean, sugar, wine, water, and cloves to saucepan and bring to boil over medium heat. Stir in kumquats and return to boil. Reduce heat, and simmer, covered, until kumquats are tender, about 5 minutes.

2 Transfer compote to bowl and cool to room temperature. Remove and discard vanilla bean and cloves. Stir in ginger. Serve at room temperature, or transfer to airtight container and refrigerate until chilled, at least 2 hours up to 4 days.

2 **SmartPoints value per serving** (⅓ cup): 68 Cal, 0 g Total Fat, 0 g Sat Fat, 6 mg Sod, 15 g Total Carb, 12 g Sugar, 3 g Fib, 1 g Prot. SmartPoints value: 2.

Tip
Serve the compote over ½ cup plain fat-free Greek yogurt for no additional SmartPoints per serving.

Sweet potato pie squares

Serves 16

Crust

1   cup graham cracker crumbs

2   tablespoons packed light brown sugar

¼   teaspoon salt

2   tablespoons unsalted butter, melted

Filling

1½   cups mashed cooked sweet potato

⅓   cup low-fat (1%) milk

⅓   cup packed light brown sugar

1   large egg

1½   teaspoons pumpkin pie spice

¼   teaspoon salt

¼   cup chopped pecans, toasted

1 Preheat oven to 350°F. Line 8-inch square baking pan with foil, extending foil over rim of pan by 2 inches; spray foil with nonstick spray.

2 Stir together crumbs, brown sugar, and salt in medium bowl. Drizzle with butter and stir to combine. Press into prepared pan. Bake 5 minutes. Maintain oven temperature.

3 Meanwhile, to make filling, whisk together sweet potato, milk, brown sugar, egg, pie spice, and salt in large bowl. Pour filling over hot crust; sprinkle with pecans. Return to oven and bake until filling is set, 50–55 minutes.

4 Cool completely in pan on wire rack. Cover and refrigerate until chilled, at least 2 hours or up to 1 day. Lift from pan using foil. Remove foil and cut bars lengthwise into 4 strips; then cut each strip across into 4 pieces.

4 **SmartPoints value per serving** (1 bar cookie): 102 Cal, 4 g Total Fat, 1 g Sat Fat, 130 mg Sod, 16 g Total Carb, 9 g Sugar, 1 g Fib, 2 g Prot.

Tip
These easy bar cookies are perfect for any fall pot luck, Halloween party, or Thanksgiving get together. Instead of mashed sweet potato, you can use canned pumpkin.

Potatoes →

Shallots →

Baby kale →

← Thyme

Chapter 5

Bonus!

Enjoy flavorful meals ready in 20 minutes or less.

Carrots

Bell peppers

In this chapter

20-minute main dishes

Lemon chicken with tomato, olive, and feta salad

Serves 4

Ingredients

4 (5-ounce) thin-sliced skinless boneless chicken cutlets

Grated zest and juice of 1 lemon

½ teaspoon salt

¼ teaspoon black pepper

1 pint grape tomatoes, halved

¼ cup pitted kalamata olives, coarsely chopped

¼ cup crumbled reduced-fat feta cheese

2 tablespoons thinly sliced fresh mint

1½ teaspoons olive oil

1 Heat ridged grill pan over medium-high heat. Sprinkle chicken with lemon zest, salt, and ⅛ teaspoon of pepper. Lightly spray chicken with olive oil nonstick spray. Place chicken in grill pan and cook, turning once, until chicken is cooked through, about 8 minutes.

2 Meanwhile, to make salad, combine lemon juice, tomatoes, olives, feta, mint, oil, and remaining ⅛ teaspoon pepper in medium bowl and toss to mix well. Serve chicken with salad.

1 **SmartPoints value per serving** (1 chicken cutlet and ½ cup salad): 230 Cal, 8 g Total Fat, 2 g Sat Fat, 512 mg Sod, 6 g Total Carb, 2 g Sugar, 2 g Fib, 34 g Prot.

Tip

Serve this versatile tomato salad with steak, fish, or shrimp. You can also add cooked pasta or grains such as barley or farro and turn it into a packable vegetarian lunch.

Grilled chicken with grapefruit-mint salsa

Serves 4

4   **(5-ounce) thin-sliced skinless boneless chicken cutlets**

½   **teaspoon ground cumin**

½   **teaspoon ground coriander**

¼   **teaspoon plus pinch salt**

⅛   **teaspoon black pepper**

2   **red grapefruit**

¼   **cup sliced fresh mint**

1   **small shallot, diced**

1   **serrano pepper, seeded and minced**

1   Spray ridged grill pan with nonstick spray and set over medium-high heat.

2   Sprinkle chicken with cumin, coriander, ¼ teaspoon of salt, and pepper. Add chicken to grill pan and cook, turning once, until chicken is lightly browned and cooked through, about 8 minutes.

3   Meanwhile, to make salsa, using serrated knife, cut thin slice from top and bottom of each grapefruit. Stand grapefruit on one end on cutting board and cut away peel and white pith. Hold fruit over medium bowl and cut along both sides of each membrane and release sections, allowing to fall into bowl. Remove any seeds. Using 2 forks, break grapefruit into small pieces. Stir in mint, shallot, serrano pepper, and remaining pinch salt.

4   Serve chicken with salsa.

0   **SmartPoints value per serving** (1 chicken cutlet and ¼ cup salsa): 216 Cal, 4 g Total Fat, 1 g Sat Fat, 283 mg Sod, 12 g Total Carb, 10 g Sugar, 2 g Fib, 33 g Prot.

Grilled chicken with
grapefruit-mint salsa

**Parmesan chicken
with fennel-arugula salad**

Parmesan chicken with fennel-arugula salad

Serves 4

1½ tablespoons lemon juice

1 tablespoon plus 1 teaspoon olive oil

¼ teaspoon honey or agave nectar

¼ teaspoon salt

½ fennel bulb, trimmed and thinly sliced

4 cups loosely packed baby arugula

¼ cup plus 2 tablespoons grated Parmesan

1 tablespoon dried seasoned bread crumbs

4 (5-ounce) thin-sliced skinless boneless chicken cutlets

1 Whisk together lemon juice, 1 tablespoon of oil, honey, and salt in large bowl. Place fennel on top, then add arugula; do not toss.

2 Combine ¼ cup of Parmesan and bread crumbs in small bowl. Place chicken on sheet of wax paper. Sprinkle half of Parmesan mixture evenly over one side of chicken cutlets and press to adhere.

3 Heat remaining 1 teaspoon of oil in large nonstick skillet over medium heat. Add chicken, coated side down. Sprinkle remaining Parmesan mixture on top of chicken. Cook, turning once, until chicken is lightly browned and cooked through, about 8 minutes.

4 Toss together salad and dressing. Divide salad among 4 plates and top evenly with chicken. Sprinkle evenly with remaining 2 tablespoons Parmesan.

3 **SmartPoints value per serving** (1 chicken cutlet and ¾ cup salad): 271 Cal, 11 g Total Fat, 3 g Sat Fat, 437 mg Sod, 6 g Total Carb, 2 g Sugar, 1 g Fib, 35 g Prot.

Chicken-vegetable noodle bowl

Serves 4

2	teaspoons finely chopped peeled fresh ginger
¾	pound thin-sliced skinless boneless chicken cutlets, cut into ¼-inch slices
4	cups reduced-sodium chicken broth
1	large carrot, shredded
1	red bell pepper, thinly sliced
6	thin scallions, thinly sliced
1	cup frozen shelled edamame
3	cups loosely packed baby spinach
1	(7.1-ounce) package precooked soba noodles
¼	cup ponzu sauce or reduced-sodium soy sauce
1	teaspoon dark (Asian) hot sesame oil
½	cup chopped fresh cilantro

1 Spray large Dutch oven with nonstick spray and set over medium-high heat. Add ginger and cook, stirring constantly until fragrant, 30 seconds. Add chicken and cook, stirring constantly, until cooked through, about 3 minutes.

2 Increase heat to high and add broth, carrot, bell pepper, scallions, and edamame. Bring to boil.

3 Stir in spinach, noodles, and ponzu sauce. Cook until heated through, 2 minutes. Remove from heat and stir in oil. Ladle soup evenly into 4 bowls and sprinkle with cilantro.

2 **SmartPoints value per serving** (2 ¼ cups): 265 Cal, 6 g Total Fat, 1 g Sat Fat, 1,058 mg Sod, 24 g Total Carb, 6 g Sugar, 4 g Fib, 30 g Prot.

Tip
If you can't find precooked soba noodles, cook 4 ounces dry soba noodles according to the package directions—it only takes about 5 minutes.

Chicken-vegetable
noodle bowl

Turkey, Swiss, and avocado panini

Serves 2

4   (1-ounce) slices multigrain
     bread

1½   tablespoons wasabi sauce

½   cup loosely packed baby spinach

1   small plum tomato, sliced

½   ripe avocado, thinly sliced

6   ounces reduced-sodium sliced
     deli turkey

2   ounces reduced-fat sliced
     Swiss cheese

1 Spread one side of bread slices with wasabi sauce. Layer 2 slices of bread evenly with spinach, tomato, avocado, turkey, and Swiss cheese. Top with remaining bread slices.

2 Spray ridged grill pan with nonstick spray and set over medium-high heat. Place sandwiches in pan and top with another heavy skillet to weight them. Cook until cheese is melted and rolls are golden brown and crispy, about 2 minutes on each side (or grill sandwiches in panini press).

10 **SmartPoints value per serving** (1 sandwich): 424 Cal, 16 g Total Fat, 3 g Sat Fat, 1,068 mg Sod, 36 g Total Carb, 6 g Sugar, 8 g Fib, 36 g Prot.

Tip
You can make your own wasabi sauce by stirring together 1½ tablespoons reduced-fat mayonnaise with 1 teaspoon prepared wasabi.

Beef, mango, and veggie wraps

Serves 4

¼   cup Asian chili-garlic sauce

1   tablespoon lime juice

½   teaspoon reduced-sodium
      soy sauce

¾   pound lean sliced deli roast beef,
      cut into ½-inch strips

16   large leaves Bibb or leaf lettuce

¼   teaspoon salt

2   large carrots, shredded

1   English (seedless) cucumber,
      halved lengthwise and sliced

1   mango, peeled, pitted, and sliced

3   scallions, sliced

¾   cup loosely packed fresh
      cilantro leaves

Lime wedges

1 To make sauce, stir together chili-garlic sauce, lime juice, and soy sauce in small bowl.

2 Divide beef among lettuce leaves and sprinkle beef with salt. Top evenly with carrots, cucumber, mango, scallions, and cilantro; roll up to enclose filling. Serve with sauce and lime wedges.

3 **SmartPoints value per serving** (4 wraps and 1½ tablespoons sauce): 220 Cal, 5 g Total Fat, 2 g Sat Fat, 906 mg Sod, 22 g Total Carb, 15 g Sugar, 4 g Fib, 23 g Prot.

Tip
Instead of roast beef, you can make these sandwiches with sliced chicken or turkey, cooked shrimp, or sliced cooked tofu.

Grilled flank steak and peppers with baby kale salad

Grilled flank steak and peppers with baby kale salad

Serves 4

1	(1-pound) lean flank steak, trimmed
4	teaspoons steak seasoning blend
1	pound mini bell peppers, left whole
1	tablespoon olive oil
2	teaspoons white balsamic vinegar
¼	teaspoon salt
⅛	teaspoon black pepper
5	cups loosely packed baby kale and spinach blend
¼	cup shaved Parmesan cheese

1 Spray grill rack with nonstick spray and preheat grill to medium-high or prepare medium-high fire.

2 Sprinkle steak with seasoning blend. Place steak and bell peppers on grill rack. Grill, turning peppers occasionally and turning steak once, until peppers are tender and instant-read thermometer inserted into center of steak registers 145°F, about 10 minutes. Transfer steak to cutting board and cut into 16 slices.

3 Whisk together oil, vinegar, salt, and pepper in large bowl. Add kale and Parmesan and toss to coat. Divide salad among 4 plates; top with steak and peppers.

6   **SmartPoints value per serving** (4 slices steak, ¾ cup peppers, and 1 cup salad): 263 Cal, 12 g Total Fat, 4 g Sat Fat, 341 mg Sod, 11 g Total Carb, 6 g Sugar, 4 g Fib, 28 g Prot.

Tip

Using whole baby peppers saves prep time, but you can substitute 3 large red or yellow bell peppers cut into 2-inch strips instead. After grilling the peppers, cut the strips into thin slices.

Middle Eastern burgers with yogurt sauce

Serves 4

1 **pound lean ground beef (7% fat or less)**

1 **shallot, finely diced**

2 **teaspoons ground coriander**

½ **plus ⅛ teaspoon salt**

1 **teaspoon ground cumin**

½ **teaspoon pumpkin pie spice**

¼ **teaspoon cayenne**

¾ **cup plain fat-free Greek yogurt**

2 **teaspoons lemon juice**

1 **teaspoon olive oil**

2 **teaspoons chopped fresh dill**

4 **(6-inch) whole- wheat pita breads, halved**

8 **Bibb lettuce leaves**

½ **English (seedless) cucumber, thinly sliced lengthwise**

½ **cup thinly sliced red onion**

1 Spray large ridged grill pan with nonstick spray and set over medium-high heat.

2 Combine beef, shallot, coriander, ½ teaspoon of salt, cumin, pie spice, and cayenne in large bowl. With damp hands, form mixture into 8 oval patties, about 3 inches long.

3 Place patties in grill pan and cook, turning once, until instant-read thermometer inserted into side of each patty registers 165°F, about 6 minutes.

4 Meanwhile, stir together yogurt, lemon juice, oil, dill, and remaining ⅛ teaspoon salt in small bowl.

5 Line pita halves with lettuce and fill evenly with burgers, cucumber, and red onion. Drizzle with yogurt sauce.

6 **SmartPoints value per serving** (2 filled pita halves): 301 Cal, 10 g Total Fat, 4 g Sat Fat, 575 mg Sod, 22 g Total Carb, 4 g Sugar, 3 g Fib, 32 g Prot.

Tip
You can use the meat mixture to make appetizer-size meatballs. To do so, shape the mixture into 1-inch balls and bake on a large rimmed baking sheet at 425°F until cooked through, about 15 minutes.

Middle Eastern burgers with yogurt sauce

**Crumb-crusted
pork with kale and
orange salad**

Crumb-crusted pork with kale and orange salad

Serves 4

¼   **cup orange juice**

5   **teaspoons Dijon mustard**

4   **teaspoons olive oil**

2   **teaspoons white-wine vinegar**

¾   **teaspoon salt**

2   **navel oranges**

6   **cups loosely packed mixed baby greens with kale**

1   **(1-pound) lean pork tenderloin, trimmed**

¼   **cup panko bread crumbs**

1 Whisk together orange juice, 1 teaspoon of mustard, 2 teaspoons of oil, vinegar, and ½ teaspoon of salt in large bowl.

2 With sharp knife, cut off slice from top and bottom of oranges. Stand fruit upright. Cut off peel and white pith, cutting from top to bottom, turning fruit as you go. Cut oranges crosswise into ½-inch rounds; cut rounds in half.

3 Place oranges and greens on top of orange juice mixture in bowl. Do not toss.

4 Cut pork in half crosswise; then cut each half lengthwise in half to make 4 pieces. Pound each piece to ¼-inch thickness. Sprinkle pork with remaining ¼ teaspoon salt. Brush with remaining 4 teaspoons mustard and sprinkle with panko, pressing to adhere.

5 Heat remaining 2 teaspoons oil in large skillet over medium-high heat. Add pork and cook, turning once, until instant-read thermometer inserted into sides of pork registers 145°F, about 6 minutes.

6 Toss salad and divide evenly among 4 plates. Top with pork and serve immediately.

5   **SmartPoints value per serving** (1 piece pork and 1½ cups salad): 250 Cal, 8 g Total Fat, 1 g Sat Fat, 747 mg Sod, 16g Total Carb, 8 g Sugar, 3 g Fib, 27 g Prot.

Cajun pork chops with pineapple-rum salsa

Serves 4

2   teaspoons Cajun seasoning

1   teaspoon paprika

4   (4-ounce) lean center-cut boneless pork loin chops, trimmed

2   tablespoons dark rum

4   teaspoons brown sugar

1½ cups diced fresh pineapple

1   plum tomato, diced

¼   small red onion, chopped

¼   cup coarsely chopped fresh cilantro

1   teaspoon chopped jalapeño pepper

Pinch salt

1 Stir together Cajun seasoning and paprika in small bowl. Rub pork chops all over with spice mixture.

2 Spray ridged grill pan with nonstick spray and set over medium-high heat. Add pork chops and cook, turning once, until instant-read thermometer inserted into sides of chops registers 145°F, 6–8 minutes.

3 Meanwhile, combine rum and brown sugar in medium bowl and stir until sugar dissolves. Add pineapple, tomato, onion, cilantro, jalapeño, and salt and stir gently to combine. Serve pork with salsa.

6 **SmartPoints value per serving** (1 pork chop and ½ cup salsa): 261 Cal, 7 g Total Fat, 1 g Sat Fat, 758 mg Sod, 14 g Total Carb, 11 g Sugar, 1 g Fib, 24 g Prot.

Tip
To save time, buy fresh pineapple already trimmed, cored, and sliced. Find it refrigerated in plastic containers in the produce department.

Grilled tuna steak sandwiches

Serves 4

4   **(4-ounce) tuna steaks (½-inch thick)**

¾   **teaspoon Old Bay seasoning**

¼   **cup reduced-fat mayonnaise**

2   **tablespoons plain fat-free Greek yogurt**

1   **tablespoon chopped fresh herbs such as dill, chives, or mint**

1½ **teaspoons grated lemon zest**

2   **teaspoons lemon juice**

4   **thin whole wheat sandwich rolls, split and toasted**

2   **cups loosely packed baby salad greens**

1   **tomato, sliced**

4   **slices red onion**

1 Spray ridged grill pan with nonstick spray and set over medium heat until hot.

2 Sprinkle tuna all over with seasoning. Place in grill pan and cook, turning once, 2–3 minutes for medium.

3 Meanwhile, stir together mayonnaise, yogurt, dill, and lemon zest and juice in small bowl.

4 Spread bottoms of rolls with mayonnaise mixture. Top each with 1 tuna steak and one-fourth of greens, tomato, and onion. Cover with tops of rolls.

5 **SmartPoints value per serving** (1 sandwich): 304 Cal, 7 g Total Fat, 1 g Sat Fat, 385 mg Sod, 27 g Total Carb, 6 g Sugar, 7 g Fib, 34 g Prot.

Fish tacos verde

Fish tacos verde

Serves 4

1 **pound tilapia or catfish fillets, cut crosswise into 1-inch strips**

1½ **teaspoons chili powder**

½ **teaspoon smoked paprika**

½ **teaspoon salt**

1 **teaspoon olive oil**

8 **(6-inch) corn tortillas, warmed**

1 **cup cherry tomatoes, quartered**

1 **cup shredded romaine lettuce**

½ **cup loosely packed fresh cilantro leaves**

½ **cup salsa verde**

Lime wedges

1 Preheat oven to 475°F. Line large baking pan with nonstick foil.

2 Place fish in large bowl. Add chili powder, paprika, and salt and drizzle with oil. Toss to coat. Arrange tilapia in single layer in prepared baking pan and bake until just opaque throughout, about 8 minutes.

3 Divide fish evenly among tortillas. Top evenly with tomatoes, lettuce, cilantro, and salsa verde. Serve with lime wedges.

3 **SmartPoints value per serving** (2 tacos): 238 Cal, 4 g Total Fat, 1 g Sat Fat, 660 mg Sod, 28 g Total Carb, 3 g Sugar, 5 g Fib, 25 g Prot.

Thai shrimp in green curry sauce

Serves 4

5	ounces thin brown rice noodles
1	teaspoon canola oil
1	large red bell pepper, thinly sliced
1	zucchini, halved lengthwise and sliced
1	pound large peeled and deveined shrimp
1	(13-ounce) can light (low-fat) coconut milk
½	cup water
1	tablespoon Asian fish sauce
1	tablespoon green curry paste
1	teaspoon honey
6	scallions, thinly sliced
⅓	cup chopped fresh basil
Lime wedges	

1 Prepare noodles according to package directions.

2 Meanwhile, heat oil in Dutch oven over medium-high heat. Add bell pepper and zucchini and cook, stirring often, until crisp-tender, about 3 minutes. Add shrimp, coconut milk, water, fish sauce, curry paste, and honey and bring to boil.

3 Stir in scallions. Cook just until shrimp are opaque in center, 1-2 minutes.

4 Divide noodles evenly among 4 bowls. Ladle soup evenly over noodles and sprinkle with basil. Serve with lime wedges.

7 **SmartPoints value per serving** (1¼ cups soup and ½ cup noodles): 314 Cal, 9 g Total Fat, 4 g Sat Fat, 1,084 mg Sod, 39 g Total Carb, 5 g Sugar, 3 g Fib, 20 g Prot.

Vegetable tortellini with tapenade

Serves 6

1   **(13-ounce) package frozen cheese tortellini**

1   **red bell pepper, chopped**

1   **large zucchini, quartered lengthwise and thinly sliced**

1   **cup frozen green peas**

2   **cups grape or cherry tomatoes, halved**

¼   **cup black olive tapenade**

1   **tablespoon white balsamic vinegar**

⅛   **teaspoon red pepper flakes**

6   **tablespoons grated Romano cheese**

¼   **cup thinly sliced fresh basil**

1 Cook tortellini according to package directions, adding bell pepper and zucchini during last 3 minutes and peas during last 1 minute of cooking time.

2 Meanwhile, place tomatoes, tapenade, vinegar, and red pepper flakes in large bowl. Drain pasta and vegetables. Add to bowl and toss to combine. Sprinkle with Romano and basil.

7   **SmartPoints value per serving** (1½ cups pasta mixture and 1 tablespoon cheese): 272 Cal, 10 g Total Fat, 4 g Sat Fat, 487 mg Sod, 40 g Total Carb, 6 g Sugar, 4 g Fib, 13 g Prot.

Tip
Instead of the tapenade, you can use sun-dried tomato pesto or basil pesto. And if you wish, substitute a large chopped tomato for the grape tomatoes.

Veggie and black bean quesadillas

Serves 4

1   **small red bell pepper, chopped**

1   **small zucchini, cut into thin strips**

½   **cup frozen corn kernels**

1   **cup canned black beans, rinsed and drained**

1½ **teaspoons chili powder**

¼   **teaspoon salt**

¼   **cup chopped fresh cilantro**

1   **cup shredded reduced-fat Mexican cheese blend**

4   **(8-inch) whole wheat flour tortillas**

½   **cup plain fat-free Greek yogurt**

½   **cup salsa**

1   Place bell pepper, zucchini, and corn in medium microwaveable bowl. Cover with wax paper and microwave on High until vegetables are crisp-tender, about 1½ minutes. Drain vegetables and stir in black beans, chili powder, salt, and cilantro.

2   Sprinkle 2 tablespoons cheese over half of each tortilla. Spoon one-fourth of vegetable mixture evenly over cheese. Sprinkle vegetables evenly with remaining cheese. Fold unfilled half of each tortilla over filling and press down lightly.

3   Heat large nonstick skillet over medium heat. Lightly spray quesadillas on both sides with nonstick spray. Cook two at a time, turning once, until crisp and heated through, about 4 minutes. Cut each quesadilla into 2 wedges and serve with yogurt and salsa.

7 **SmartPoints value per serving** (1 quesadilla, 2 tablespoons yogurt, and 2 tablespoons salsa): 318 Cal, 10 g Total Fat, 5 g Sat Fat, 1,122 mg Sod, 39 g Total Carb, 5 g Sugar, 8 g Fib, 19 g Prot.

Tip

If you'd like to spice up the quesadillas, add some chopped pickled jalapeños, a few teaspoons minced chipotles en adobo, or a dash or two of hot sauce to the vegetables along with the chili powder in step 1.

Veggie and
black bean
quesadillas

**Spice crusted roast pork tenderloin
with watercress salad, 31**

Recipes by SmartPoints value

0 SmartPoints value

Asian spaghetti squash salad, 186
Grilled chicken with grapefruit-mint salsa, 224

1 SmartPoints value

Arctic char with tarragon leeks, 36
Butternut squash with hoisin, 192
Chicken and eggplant stir-fry with snow peas, 84
Chilled mint-pea soup with lemon yogurt, 12
Fall fruit and yogurt breakfast bowls, 121
Greek grilled fish and vegetable kebabs, 96
Greek yogurt with warm blueberry sauce, 66
Grilled chicken with mint chimichurri, 25
Grilled tuna with blood orange salsa, 206
Lemon chicken witn tomato, olive, and feta salad, 223
Lemon-marinated grilled summer squash with dill, 80
Moroccan chicken with oranges, 193
Roasted cauliflower "steaks" with tomato-basil vinaigrette, 135
Skillet cod and summer vegetables, 98
Summer vegetable frittata, 58
Tandoori roasted salmon and vegetables, 95

2 SmartPoints value

African-style vegetable curry, 207
Chicken with roasted grape sauce, 138
Chicken-vegetable noodle bowl, 228
Dijon-roasted salmon with fall vegetables, 153
Greek yogurt with cherry compote and pistachios, 62
Grilled Asian chicken with carrot-cucumber slaw, 81
Israeli couscous with tomato and olive sauté, 79
Kumquat and ginger compote, 218
Melon with ginger-mint syrup, 108
Orange-scented turnips and greens, 136
Pear and fig salad with blue cheese, 129
Pumpkin-ginger bisque, 128
Roasted beet and carrot salad, 130
Ruby winter vegetable soup, 181
Smoky corn soup, 70
Spring garden vegetable soup, 11
Thai turkey and broccoli stir-fry, 141

3 SmartPoints value

Asian peanut chicken salad, 71
Beef, mango, and veggie wraps, 231
Black bean, farro, and roasted squash chili, 157
Blackberry cheesecake tarts, 103

Carrot-coconut oatmeal cookies, 215
Cinnamon French toast with raspberries, 61
Egg, bacon, and greens breakfast sandwiches, 172
Fava bean sandwiches, 17
Fish tacos verde, 241
Five-spice pork tenderloin with ginger plums, 91
Freekeh with roasted tomatoes and fava beans, 20
Frittata with Brussels sprouts and bacon, 171
Greek yogurt with rhubarb-raspberry spoon fruit, 50
Green breakfast smoothie, 7
Late-summer southwest turkey and vegetable soup, 67
Lentil and chorizo soup with kale, 125
Parmesan chicken with fennel-arugula salad, 227
Parsnip-pear mini cupcakes with cream cheese frosting, 211
Peach, tomato, and avocado salad, 73
Red curry tofu and vegetable bowls, 158
Roasted Brussels sprouts with cranberries and walnuts, 191
Skillet ratatouille with eggs, 56
Slow-cooker lamb, chickpea, and squash stew, 147
Strawberry-mandarin granita, 51
Sweet potato–spice truffles, 166
Watercress salad with grapefruit and papaya, 14

4 SmartPoints value

Blender gazpacho with avocado, 68
Bunless Asian beef burger wraps, 88
Citrus olive oil cake, 216
Filets mignons with spring onion salsa verde, 28
Ginger shrimp with soba-spinach sauté, 154
Grilled Caesar salad with cherry tomatoes, 74
Grilled chicken with peach bbq sauce, 82
Ham and goat cheese frittata with spring vegetables, 5
Indian-spiced lamb chops with fresh mint sauce, 33
Lemon angel food cake with strawberry-balsamic compote, 44
Lemon-rosemary chicken with radicchio, 198
Plum and blackberry crisp with pistachio crumble, 107
Pork tenderloin with lentils and winter squash, 149
Quinoa with fresh peas and mint, 19
Roasted whole chicken with apples and sausage, 194
Rosemary chicken with pears and leeks, 137
Rosemary steak with apple-horseradish relish, 200
Sausage, kale, and Cheddar frittata, 116
Scrambled egg, goat cheese, and tomato sandwiches, 55
Spice-crusted roast pork tenderloin with watercress salad, 31
Sweet potato pie squares, 219

5 SmartPoints value

Almond-cherry oat bars, 111
Asparagus and pea pancakes, 3
Beef, cauliflower, and edamame curry, 146
Bulgur salad with fennel, radish, and basil, 13
Cajun shrimp with garlicky spinach grits, 204
Crumb-crusted pork with kale and orange salad, 237
Flank steak with cherry tomatoes and basil, 87
Gemelli with tomatoes, limas, and arugula pesto, 102
Grilled coffee-rubbed steak with pear-cranberry salsa, 144
Grilled tuna steak sandwiches, 239
Grilled tuna with cucumber-noodle salad, 35
Kale salad with sweet potato and coconut, 184
Lamb chops with cucumber-mint salad, 32
Penne with roasted cauliflower and feta, 209
Pomegranate-papaya smoothie, 180
Pork chops with apples and ginger, 203
Prosciutto, kale, and mozzarella melts, 133
Roasted chicken with artichokes and potatoes, 22
Singapore noodles with tofu and vegetables, 41
Slow-cooker chicken with celery root and rosemary, 140
Smoky sweet potato and black bean soup, 127
Wheat berry-apple salad, 187
White bean and quinoa cakes, 101

6 SmartPoints value

Almond breakfast quinoa with kumquats, 176
Blueberry-peach cornmeal cupcakes, 104
Butternut squash tart with candied pecans, 163
Cajun pork chops with pineapple-rum salsa, 238
Carrot-parsnip soup, 183
Chicken and vegetables with balsamic-espresso glaze, 197
Fruit orchard oatmeal, 179
Gingerbread pancakes with pears, 119
Gingery winter squash custards with gingersnap crumble, 212
Grilled flank steak and peppers with baby kale salad, 233
Grilled vegetables and polenta, 99
Middle Eastern burgers with yogurt sauce, 234
Pasta and spring vegetables with feta, 39
Plum and ricotta trifle with almonds, 110
Raspberry-peach smoothies, 65
Rhubarb-strawberry shortcakes, 47
Spicy turkey, apple, and spinach panini, 189
Steak with balsamic-molasses sauce and roasted green beans, 85
Sweet potato muffins with pecan streusel, 115
White bean pita burgers with yogurt-tahini sauce, 77

7 SmartPoints value

Apple-cranberry muffins, 178
Baked ricotta puddings with grapes, 165
Blueberry-almond muesli, 59
Grilled Mediterranean chicken and vegetable wraps, 78
Irish oatmeal with brown sugar–cinnamon roasted apples, 122
Orecchiette with sausage and broccoli rabe, 143
Thai shrimp in green curry sauce, 242
Vegetable tortellini with tapenade, 243
Veggie and black bean quesadillas, 244
Warm chai rice pudding with mango, 43
Whole-grain mango muffins, 6

8 SmartPoints value

Apple streusel crostata, 164
Buttermilk waffles with oranges and pomegranate, 175
Carrot-apple Bundt cake with cream cheese glaze, 160
Chocolate berry pavlova, 48
Grilled chicken with couscous-mango salad, 21
Grilled chicken, broccoli rabe, and Peppadew sandwiches, 190
Maple muesli with apples and pecans, 124
Open-face prosciutto, avocado, and arugula sandwiches, 18
Penne primavera, 42
Slow-cooker Middle Eastern beef stew, 199
Stuffed pork chops with creamy mustard sauce, 150

9 SmartPoints value

Cranberry-almond cupcakes, 159
Cranberry-pear breakfast porridge, 120
Ginger breakfast cakes with quick strawberry jam, 8
Goat cheese polenta with spring vegetables, 40

10 SmartPoints value

Broccoli and Cheddar mac and cheese, 210
Chutney chicken sliders, 26
Turkey, Swiss, and avocado panini, 230

11 SmartPoints value

Flatbread prosciutto and salad pizza, 92

12 SmartPoints value

Chicken sausage and mushroom hoagies, 134

Index

Flatbread prosciutto and salad pizza, 92

Measurement equivalents

If you are converting the recipes in this book to metric measurements, use the following chart as a guide.

Teaspoons	Tablespoons	Cups	Fluid ounces
3 teaspoons	1 tablespoon		½ fluid ounce
6 teaspoons	2 tablespoons	⅛ cup	1 fluid ounce
8 teaspoons	2 tablespoons plus 2 teaspoons	⅙ cup	
12 teaspoons	4 tablespoons	¼ cup	2 fluid ounces
15 teaspoons	5 tablespoons	⅓ cup minus 1 teaspoon	
16 teaspoons	5 tablespoons plus 1 teaspoon	⅓ cup	
18 teaspoons	6 tablespoons	¼ cup plus 2 tablespoons	3 fluid ounces
24 teaspoons	8 tablespoons	½ cup	4 fluid ounces
30 teaspoons	10 tablespoons	½ cup plus 2 tablespoons	5 fluid ounces
32 teaspoons	10 tablespoons plus 2 teaspoons	⅔ cup	
36 teaspoons	12 tablespoons	¾ cup	6 fluid ounces
42 teaspoons	14 tablespoons	1 cup minus 2 tablespoons	7 fluid ounces
45 teaspoons	15 tablespoons	1 cup minus 1 tablespoon	
48 teaspoons	16 tablespoons	1 cup	8 fluid ounces

Volume	
¼ teaspoon	1 milliliter
½ teaspoon	2 milliliters
1 teaspoon	5 milliliters
1 tablespoon	15 milliliters
2 tablespoons	30 milliliters
3 tablespoons	45 milliliters
¼ cup	60 milliliters
⅓ cup	80 milliliters
½ cup	120 milliliters
⅔ cup	160 milliliters
¾ cup	175 milliliters
1 cup	240 milliliters
1 quart	950 milliliters

Length	
1 inch	25 millimeters
1 inch	2.5 centimeters

Oven temperature			
250°F	120°C	400°F	200°C
275°F	140°C	425°F	220°C
300°F	150°C	450°F	230°C
325°F	160°C	475°F	250°C
350°F	180°C	500°F	260°C
375°F	190°C	525°F	270°C

Weight	
1 ounce	30 grams
¼ pound	120 grams
½ pound	240 grams
¾ pound	340 grams
1 pound	480 grams

Note: Measurement of less than ⅛ teaspoon is considered a dash or a pinch. Metric measurements are approximate.